HEALTHCARE ACTIVE LEARNING

HAL

DESCRIPTIVE STATISTICS

Start date

Target completion date

Tutor for this topic

Contact number

USING THIS WORKBOOK

The workbook is divided into 'Sessions', covering specific subjects.

In the introduction to each learning pack there is a learner profile to help you assess your current knowledge of the subjects covered in each session.

Each session has clear learning objectives. They indicate what you will be able to achieve or learn by completing that session.

Each session has a summary to remind you of the key points of the subjects covered.

Each session contains text, diagrams and learning activities that relate to the stated objectives.

It is important to complete each activity, making your own notes and writing in answers in the space provided. **Remember this is your own workbook—you are allowed to write on it**.

Now try an example activity.

ACTIVITY

This activity shows you what happens when cells work without oxygen. This really is a physical activity, so please only try it if you are fully fit.

First, raise one arm straight up in the air above your head, and let the other hand rest by your side. Clench both fists tightly, and then open out your fingers wide. Repeat this at the rate of once or twice a second. Try to keep clenching both fists at the same rate. Keep going for about five minutes, and record what you observe.

Stop and rest for a minute. Then try again, with the opposite arm raised this time. Again, record your observations.

⬇

Suggested timings are given for each activity. These are only a guide. You may like to note how long it took you to complete this activity, as it may help in planning the time needed for working through the sessions.

⬇

Time taken on activity

⬇

Time management is important. While we recognise that people learn at different speeds, this pack is designed to take 15 study hours (your tutor will also advise you). You should allocate time during each week for study.

⬇

Take some time now to identify likely periods that you can set aside for study during the week.

	Mon	Tues	Wed	Thurs	Fri	Sat	Sun
am							
pm							
eve							

⬇

At the end of the learning pack, there is a learning review to help you assess whether you have achieved the learning objectives.

HAL
HEALTHCARE ACTIVE LEARNING

DESCRIPTIVE STATISTICS

Hugh Miller BA PhD

Principal Lecturer in Applied Social Studies, The Nottingham Trent University

THE OPEN LEARNING FOUNDATION

CHURCHILL LIVINGSTONE

EDINBURGH HONG KONG LONDON MADRID MELBOURNE NEW YORK AND TOKYO 1995

CHURCHILL LIVINGSTONE
Medical Division of Longman Group UK Limited

Distributed in the United States of America by Churchill
Livingstone Inc., 650 Avenue of the Americas, New York,
N.Y. 10011, and by associated companies, branches and
representatives throughout the world.

First published 1995

ISBN 0 443 05341 3

British Library of Cataloguing in Publication Data
A catalogue record for this book is available from the
British Library.

Library of Congress Cataloging in Publication Data
A catalogue record for this book is available from the
Library of Congress

Produced through Longman Malaysia, TCP.

For The Open Learning Foundation

Director of Programmes: Leslie Mapp
Series Editor: Robert Adams
Programmes Manager: Kathleen Farren
Production Manager: Steve Moulds

For Churchill Livingstone

Director (Nursing and Allied Health): Peter Shepherd
Project Development Editor: Mairi McCubbin
Project Manager: Valerie Burgess
Design Direction: Judith Wright
Sales Promotion Executive: Hilary Brown

Contents

OPEN LEARNING FOUNDATION TEAM MEMBERS

Writer: Hugh Miller BA PhD
Principal Lecturer in Applied Social Studies
The Nottingham Trent University

Editor: Howard Freeman
CETD,
De Montfort University

Reviewer: Colin Stevenson
Consultant in Public Health Medicine,
West Midlands Regional Health Authority

Series Editor: Robert Adams
OLF Programme Head,
Social Work and Health and Nursing,
University of Humberside

THE OPEN LEARNING FOUNDATION

Higher education has grown considerably in recent years. As well as catering for more students, universities are facing the challenge of providing for an increasingly diverse student population. Students have a wider range of backgrounds and previous educational qualifications. There are greater numbers of mature students. There is a greater need for part-time courses and continuing education and professional development programmes.

The Open Learning Foundation helps over 20 member institutions meet this growing and diverse demand – through the production of high-quality teaching and learning materials, within a strategy of creating a framework for more flexible learning. It offers member institutions the capability to increase their range of teaching options and to cover subjects in greater breadth and depth.

It does not enrol its own students. Rather, The Open Learning Foundation, by developing and promoting the greater use of open and distance learning, enables universities and others in higher education to make study more accessible and cost-effective for individual students and for business through offering more choice and more flexible courses.

Formed in 1990, the Foundation's policy objectives are to:

- improve the quality of higher education and training

- increase the quantity of higher education and training

- raise the efficiency of higher education and training delivery.

In working to meet these objectives, The Open Learning Foundation develops new teaching and learning materials, encourages and facilitates more and better staff development, and promotes greater responsiveness to change within higher education institutions. The Foundation works in partnership with its members and other higher education bodies to develop new approaches to teaching and learning.

In developing new teaching and learning materials, the Foundation has:

- a track record of offering customers a swift and flexible response

- a national network of members able to provide local support and guidance

- the ability to draw on significant national expertise in producing and delivering open learning

- complete freedom to seek out the best writers, materials and resources to secure development.

INTRODUCTION

This unit is about descriptive statistics, where numbers are used to summarise information about the world. Look in any newspaper, magazine or journal and you'll see charts, graphs, tables and diagrams being used in an attempt to reduce the vast amount of data that we generate to a digestible whole. Descriptive statistics can help us with this task.

Inferential statistics is a related area that uses statistical techniques to help form judgements – to draw *inferences*, for example, as to whether a particular result or observation could have arisen by chance, or whether it signifies a real process or difference between groups.

The most important things about statistics are what they mean and what they can be used for, not how they are calculated. Because of this there is very little maths in this unit, and any calculations will be the kind that can be done in your head or on a scrap of paper. Having a calculator handy would save a little effort, but it isn't essential.

As you work through the unit you will come across a number of activities which are designed to guide your learning. Although you will find that a time allowance has been included for each of these, you should only regard it as a very rough estimate and not be concerned if the activity takes you less or more time than indicated. It is a good idea to keep a notebook or file of your work on activities: in some instances you will be asked to refer back to your answers earlier in the unit.

All of the terms and concepts which are introduced during this unit are highlighted in the text and defined in the margin. This is not always at their very first appearance – for instance they may have featured in a heading or introductory paragraph – but at a point where they first form part of the main text or when you first need to refer to them. The glossary at the end gives the terms and definitions again in alphabetical order. If you are still in doubt about any of the ideas which are discussed, you should consult one of the books which are listed in the Further Reading section at the end of the unit.

Session One examines the way we measure things, and identifies three groups of measures: categories, rankings and quantity measures. I'll also take a look behind the data to question the reliability and credibility of its origins.

Session Two is about building up a practical idea of what descriptive statistics are and where you're likely to come across them, and discusses in general what they are used for.

Session Three aims to show you how statistics can help in understanding large collections of information by organising them and simplifying them so that it becomes possible to see the overall picture. You'll be given a large block of information and asked to find ways of representing it statistically. You'll also be asked about what the representations might show – what questions about the data a statistical presentation could help to answer. The rest of the session will be about the strengths and weaknesses of various kinds of statistical presentation in representing the data.

Session Four is about ways of summing up data in one or two numbers using methods such as the mean, the median and the mode.

Session Five is concerned with overall patterns in the data – distribution.

Session Six looks at ways to describe variation in a collection of measurements – what's called measures of dispersion.

Session Seven is about ways of describing relationships between sets of data – the idea of correlation.

Session Eight concentrates on graphs and other pictorial presentations – how they can help in understanding the data and how they may mislead.

Session Nine, the conclusion, has an activity that will help you to sum up the general points and principles of the unit as a whole.

LEARNING PROFILE

Given below is a list of learning outcomes for each session in this unit. You can use it to identify your current learning, and consider how the unit can help you to develop your knowledge and understanding. The list is not intended to cover all of the details discussed in every session, so the learning profile should only be used for general guidance.

For each of the learning outcomes listed below, tick the box that corresponds most closely to the point you feel you are at now. This will provide you with an assessment of your current understanding and confidence in the areas that you will study in this unit.

	Not at all	Partly	Quite well	Very well

Session One

I can:

- explain that the reliability of data may be influenced by many factors ☐ ☐ ☐ ☐
- identify category, ranking and quantity measures ☐ ☐ ☐ ☐
- distinguish between interval and ratio scales. ☐ ☐ ☐ ☐

Session Two

I can:

- identify the various forms which statistical presentations may take ☐ ☐ ☐ ☐
- describe typical purposes for presenting information statistically. ☐ ☐ ☐ ☐

	Not at all	Partly	Quite well	Very well

Session Three

I can:

- understand the importance of clearly defining what information I wish to obtain from data $\square$ $\square$ $\square$ $\square$
- group and rearrange data in a table in order to make sense of large amounts of information $\square$ $\square$ $\square$ $\square$
- identify ways of organising data and presenting it graphically using frequency distributions, pie charts and scattergrams. $\square$ $\square$ $\square$ $\square$

Session Four

I can:

- describe three main measures of central tendency: the mean, the mode and the median $\square$ $\square$ $\square$ $\square$
- explain the ways in which these measures are affected by changes in the data $\square$ $\square$ $\square$ $\square$
- select the most appropriate measure for particular purposes. $\square$ $\square$ $\square$ $\square$

Session Five

I can:

- use frequency distributions for summarising and presenting data $\square$ $\square$ $\square$ $\square$
- appreciate that the shape of a distribution is determined by the processes giving rise to it $\square$ $\square$ $\square$ $\square$
- describe typical deviations from ideal forms, such as skewedness, humps and dips, and be able to suggest reasons for them. $\square$ $\square$ $\square$ $\square$

Session Six

I can:

- understand that different sets of data have different degrees of internal variability $\square$ $\square$ $\square$ $\square$
- define the terms quartile, decile, and percentile $\square$ $\square$ $\square$ $\square$
- understand the way in which the standard deviation may be used to represent the variability in a set of figures $\square$ $\square$ $\square$ $\square$

	Not at all	Partly	Quite well	Very well

Session Six *continued*

I can:

- determine how common or rare a given value is compared to the overall sample from which it comes by using the standard deviation.

| | ☐ | ☐ | ☐ | ☐ |

Session Seven

I can:

- use scattergrams to detect trends and patterns in sets of data

| | ☐ | ☐ | ☐ | ☐ |

- describe the use of the correlation coefficient as a measure of the agreement between two sets of measures

| | ☐ | ☐ | ☐ | ☐ |

- state the meaning of positive and negative correlation

| | ☐ | ☐ | ☐ | ☐ |

- explain why the correlation coefficient does not always accurately represent the relationships between sets of observations

| | ☐ | ☐ | ☐ | ☐ |

- appreciate that correlation coefficients do not imply any causal relationship between factors.

| | ☐ | ☐ | ☐ | ☐ |

Session Eight

I can:

- give three reasons for the graphical presentation of statistical data

| | ☐ | ☐ | ☐ | ☐ |

- select appropriate graphical presentations for various statistical purposes

| | ☐ | ☐ | ☐ | ☐ |

- describe two techniques which can be used to distort the impressions given in graphical presentations.

| | ☐ | ☐ | ☐ | ☐ |

Measures and measurement

Introduction

Before looking at the representation of data you should examine the quality of the measurements that lie behind it. It is a mistake to assume that all measurements are equally accurate or credible: you just have to think of common examples like the accuracy of the change you get in a shop to see the point. You'll examine this issue in your first activity.

We also need to consider the meaning of the word measure. We can measure both foot size and temperature easily, but while we will accept a temperature value of 98.4°F, we would balk if offered a shoe of size 7.35. We'll discuss the different types of measure and the difference between ratio and interval scales in this session.

Session objectives

At the end of this session you should be able to:

- explain that the reliability of data may be influenced by many factors

- identify category, ranking and quantity measures

- distinguish between interval and ratio scales.

How accurate is your data?

Data *is the set of information that is being studied or statistically analysed.*

The statistics we will be examining all result from analysing **data**. But this data first of all has to be gathered and collected and in this collection process there are a number of opportunities for misunderstandings, questionable assumptions or mistakes to occur. The following activity illustrates this.

ACTIVITY 1   ALLOW 10 MINUTES

Factors that may affect the accuracy and reliability of the reported rate of a disease

Suppose statistics are collected from doctors recording the occurrence of a certain complaint such as food poisoning. Make a list of those factors which you think may cause the reported figures to differ from the actual incidence of the disease.

Commentary:

Here are some possibilities, you may have more.

- Do all doctors record the information and pass it on? Legislation (about notifiable diseases) and the efficiency of the local bureaucracy may affect the results here.

- Do the same symptoms always get the same diagnosis? Publicity about the risks of food poisoning may affect how ambiguous symptoms are diagnosed.

Others are to do with whether people present themselves as cases or not.

- Do sufferers think doctors can help them? If people don't expect effective treatment, they won't bother to go to the doctor and won't appear in the statistics.

- Are there other reasons for sufferers to seek out or avoid doctors? Employers' rules about sick leave and doctor's certificates may encourage people to visit the doctor. The cost of consultation or medication may discourage people from consulting the doctor about what they may see as a minor problem.

- Are there other sources of treatment? Traditional remedies or pharmacists may deflect people from seeking medical help.

- People may not even think that they're ill. Nausea may be put down to other causes, like over-indulgence in adults and over-excitement in children.

After all this, it might be difficult to have faith in statistics at all. However, some other cases might be more straightforward, or it might be possible to limit the frame of reference to be more specific. So although there may be all kinds of variations in presentation and diagnosis, it might be possible to give a reliable account of the outcomes of treatment for those who had been diagnosed.

In any case, incomplete or imperfect information can still be very useful. It is clearly better than no information at all. It is just necessary to be aware of the possible shortcomings of that information.

For the rest of this unit I'll ignore these problems, but they are worth bearing in mind when it comes to interpreting real-life statistics.

Categories, ranking and quantity measures

Not all measures are of the same kind. Three main kinds are usually distinguished: categories, rankings and numerical (or quantity) measures.

Categories might not look like measures at all, but they are useful ways of organising information. If someone recorded the incidence of different illnesses, or the proportions of workers of different grades in a unit, the illnesses and the grades would be examples of categorical information. Another name for this kind of measure is a **nominal measure**.

Ranking is a way of organising observations in order: from least to most, best to worst, etc., without being very precise about the distances between points on that order. A medical example is the APGAR scale on which the well-being of infants at birth is rated. A high score gives less cause for concern than a low score, but it's not clear that a rating of 8 is twice as good as 4, or the difference between 3 and 6 is the same as the difference between 6 and 9. You could even claim that the APGAR scale doesn't even lead to reliable rankings and it's really a collection of

*A **category** variable is a measure which consists of putting observations into different groups, without any ranking or quantitative aspect. Recording numbers of complaints according to whether they occur in medical, surgical, accident and emergency or community practice is an example of using a category distinction.*

*A **nominal scale** is a scale of measurement which is based on categories alone, with no value or ranking attached to the measure.*

A **rank** *variable is a measure that assigns observations to an order from first to last, highest to lowest or most to least. Recording staff rank or seniority, or ratings of waiting rooms on a scale of comfort, are examples of using rank variables.*

An **ordinal scale** *is a scale of measurement which is based on ranking variables. This should give information about which is greater or lesser, first or last, but without any information about the size of the difference between ranks.*

A **quantity** *variable is a measure which consists of assigning a numerical value to an observation, so that calculations and arithmetical comparisons with other values can justifiably be made. Recording the number of staff working in different units, the temperature of different environments, or the time between surgery and discharge are all examples of using quantity variables. Quantity variables can be subdivided into those based on interval scales and those based on ratio scales.*

categorical measures rather than a scale. It would be possible for two infants both to be rated at 6 even though they showed very different responses.

Another measure which is most accurately considered as a ranking is academic marks. 75% for an essay is better than 50%, but the gap between 25% and 50% probably has a different meaning than the gap between 50% and 75%. Gaining more GCSEs seems a better academic achievement than gaining less, but the difference between getting 10 and getting 12 is probably not the same as the difference between getting one and getting three. Measures which are based on rankings like this are called **ordinal** measures.

Some measures use numbers in what seems to be a more consistent way: 500g is twice as much as 250g, and the difference between 500g and 750g is the same as the difference between 1,000g and 1250g. An interest payment of 20% on a £1,000 loan is twice as much as a 10% payment on the same loan. These are **quantity** measures, and there are two kinds based on **interval** and **ratio** scales. The examples I've given here, of weight and percentage, use ratio scales. Equal-sized steps in the measure represent equal-sized changes in amount and a doubling of the measure indicates a doubling of the amount.

For interval scales, only the first is true: equal *intervals* represent equal changes. The ratio between two measures does not correspond to the *ratio* between the amounts measured so they don't qualify as ratio scales. An example is either of the two everyday temperature scales. Twenty degrees centigrade (or Celsius) is not twice as hot as 10 degrees centigrade, or 20 times as hot as one degree centigrade. This becomes even more obvious when you compare the figures with the rough Fahrenheit equivalents: 68°F, 50°F and 34°F. The intervals in the temperature scales do represent constant intervals in the quantity measured, though: the amount of heat required to change the temperature of a body by 10°C is the same whatever its starting temperature.

Category, ranking and quantity measures all have their place in descriptive statistics. Some statistics are more appropriate for one kind of measure than others. We will meet examples of each of them later in the unit.

ACTIVITY 2

ALLOW **10** MINUTES

Different kinds of measures

Use the blank table opposite to summarise your knowledge of the measures introduced in this session. Fill the first column or two with the examples used so far, then add the given examples to the table, then fill in one or two columns of your own.

Measure	Example	Example	Example	Example
Category	Different types of music			
Ranking				
Quantity (interval/ratio)				

Examples to classify:
- different types of music
- strength of coffee
- strength of wine (percentage alcohol)
- university degrees, diplomas and certificates
- speed (velocity) of an African swallow.

Commentary:

The first example, different types of music, is a category measure. The strength of coffee, if described as strong, medium or weak, is a rank measure. On the other hand, if strength were measured as the weight of coffee powder added to a fixed quantity of liquid, it would be a ratio measure. Strength of wine measured by the percentage of alcohol is a ratio measure. University degrees, diplomas and certificates are different kinds of qualification and so are category measures. But, if you take into account that students usually study for one year for certificate, two years for diploma and three years for a degree, then they could be considered examples of rank measure. As with coffee strength, exactly how the measure is defined will affect what kind of measure it is. Flying velocity is a quantity measured on a ratio scale: 40mph is twice as fast as 20mph, and the difference in velocity between 0 and 20mph is the same as that between 80 and 100mph.

Another distinction that can be made is between continuous data, in which all values are possible, and discrete data, which can only take on certain values. Weight is a measure that could be used for continuous data. A can of beans may contain at least 464 grams, according to the label. But, if I am concerned about precise amounts, I might find that one can contains 465 grams, another 465.3, another 467.1 – or even more precisely 467.0937 grams. With careful and precise methods finer distinctions can be made.

In contrast, a measure based on the number of people in a queue is discrete. It can only take on certain values. It is possible that 1, 2, 3 or 70 people are in a queue, but it would not make sense to say there are 3.0937 people waiting in line.

The form of measurement used is important in deciding whether data is continuous or discrete. From a quality control point of view, the weight of beans in a can is a continuous measure. From the point of view of shoppers and supermarket shelf stackers, the size of the can is a discrete variable with four values: small, medium, large and catering. You will find examples of both continuous measures (height and weight) and discrete ones (numbers of people) as you work through this unit.

Summary

1. So far we've looked at some of the many factors which affect the reliability of statistical information, in particular the way that information is collected.

2. We have identified the three main kinds of measure: category (or nominal), ranking and quantity measures. Different statistical treatments are sometimes appropriate for the different types of measure.

3. There are two kinds of quantity measure: interval and ratio.

Before you move on to Session Two, check that you have achieved the objectives given at the beginning of this session, and, if not, review the appropriate sections.

SESSION TWO

About statistics

Introduction

How are statistics represented and used? One way to answer this question is to find some examples: the first exercise asks you to find a range of examples and group them into different categories.

In order to complete this session you'll need a newspaper, a professional magazine and a journal such as *Nature*, *Scientific American* or the journal of any scientific body.

Session objectives

At the end of this session you should be able to:

- identify the various forms which statistical presentations may take

- describe typical purposes for presenting information statistically.

Looking at different presentations

We are surrounded by examples of descriptive statistics. On television and in newspapers and magazines, information is presented in the form of charts, diagrams and figures. All of them are trying to convey information or offer a particular picture of the world.

ACTIVITY 3　　　　　　　　　ALLOW **20** MINUTES

How statistics are used

Examine a variety of sources for **anything** which tries to represent what happens in the world in numbers, tables, or graphs. Your sources might include:

● a newspaper, the broadsheets such as the *Times*, *Guardian* and *Financial Times* are probably better for this exercise

● a magazine such as your trade union magazine, *Which?* or the *Economist*

● a journal such as the *British Journal of Nursing*, *Nature* or *New Scientist*.

The important point is to use as wide a range of sources as possible.

List three or four examples of these 'statistical representations' from each source.

Organise the examples into different groups. Possible headings might be basic figures, percentages, summaries, averages, graphs and charts.

Commentary:

Of course, the news for the period the publications cover will make a difference to what you find; elections, budgets, and economic crises, in particular, have their own sets of statistics. Even so, you are likely to come across a very wide range of examples. Here's what I found...

Newspaper

Graph of bank interest rates.

Percentage changes in interest rates.

Stock Market indicators: FTSE and Dow Jones.

Numbers of workers losing jobs and being taken on.

Amounts of money available for government road building schemes.

Figures on average temperature and rainfall.

Predictions of numbers of people and amounts of money involved in social security changes.

Numbers and percentages on amount of sick leave taken by people in 'boring' and 'non-boring' jobs.

Discussion of percentage pay rises.

Different VAT rates (in percentages) around Europe, and the effect VAT changes might have on newspaper sales (numbers of papers and sales in millions).

Changes in unemployment figures and the effect that has on government spending.

Two pie charts (UK and European truck markets) and several tables of various rates, prices and indices.

Magazine

Discussion of an election with turnout figures in numbers and percentages, and numbers of votes needed to elect representatives in different parts of the country.

Percentages of wards meeting specified standards.

Total and average costs of accidents at work.

Graph of deaths from volatile substance abuse over the last 20 years.

Several short research reports, quoting numbers and percentages of subjects taking part and affected in various ways, and rates per 10,000 in different countries.

Journal

Percentage increase in use of child health hotline.

Proportions of different age groups suffering visual impairment.

Changes in the proportion of people over 65 in the population over time.

Significant and non-significant increases in risk of breast cancer with hormone replacement therapy.

These examples can be divided into several classes of presentation.

Basic figures

700 workers lose jobs; new road costs £31.3m; 13 out of 17 patients showed improvement.

Percentages, changes in percentages, and percentage changes

50% fail to meet basic standards; 7% base rate; interest rates fall 2%; 55% increase.

Summaries

So many per 10,000 of population; stock market indices calculated from figures for many individual companies.

Averages

Average temperature; average cost in different regions; average pay increase for workers.

Graphs and charts

Line graphs of death rates over time; table of company names, stock prices, and changes; weather maps; pie charts of market share.

There were no bar charts in my sample, but there may be in yours.

You may have organised your example slightly differently. That's OK: there are many ways of categorising statistics. The point of the exercise is to show the wide range of statistical presentations which appear in material that you're likely to read and use, and to provide you with examples to use in the next activity.

Some journals will have statements about the 'statistical significance' of results reported in the articles. Issues of statistical significance are the concern of inferential statistics and aren't covered in this unit.

Reasons for using statistics

The authors and editors of the publications you looked at chose to use statistics for various reasons. Can we identify and categorise them? The next activity tries to answer this question.

ACTIVITY 4   ALLOW **20** MINUTES

The purpose of statistical presentations

Look through the examples of statistical presentations that you picked out in *Activity 3* and reorganise them by their function. For example, they may be there as statements of fact, as comparisons or as economical ways to list a lot of data. Use these categories and any others that occur to you to group the presentations into categories.

Commentary:

Since we're speculating about the aims of the original writers, there's a wide range of categories we could come up with. If your list is at all different from mine perhaps you could see if you can re-categorise your examples to fit my headings, then try to fit my examples to your list.

Plain reporting: 'This is what happened; this is how much it cost.'

Comparison between different groups or areas: 'This is the rate in the USA, this is the rate in the UK.'

Making a case, supporting an argument: 'Have you realised that only 3% of cases are cured?'

Organising a mass of varied information so that people can find the bit they want: Share price tables.

Showing trends and patterns: How the value of the pound, or the death-rate from substance abuse, has changed over the years.

Giving an idea of what is 'normal' or 'representative': Average weather statistics, average pay. ('Normal' and 'representative' are in quotes because they're not straightforward terms. 'Normal' has lots of meanings, including a statistical one, and averages may not represent the original information at all well. We'll discuss this issue later in Sessions Four and Five.)

Giving an idea of what is 'abnormal' or extreme: Highest tides for 30 years, richer than 99.5% of the population.

Misleading the reader, or just 'blinding them with figures': Perhaps it's not fair on the authors for me to pick out specific examples, but you may have felt that this applies to some of your examples. In later sessions of the unit, particularly Session Eight, we will examine some confusing and misleading presentations.

If you look back over what you found in *Activities 3* and *4*, you will probably find some examples and uses which are different from mine. This doesn't matter because the point here is that numbers are commonly used in representing and understanding the world, and there are many reasons for using these representations.

Nearly all the examples from this exercise could be called 'statistics'. Even a single figure could be regarded as a statistic – for example, 'I spent £42 at the supermarket last week' – especially if it is put into a wider context:

'That was half of my family's weekly expenditure on food. We spend 15% of our family income on food, much less than the 21% given as the figure for UK families in *Social Trends 22* (HMSO 1992).'

In this unit I will consider any numerical or graphical representation of things that happen in the world as a statistic, though I will concentrate on those that set out to simplify, summarise, or organise the information.

Summary

1. This session examined and categorised some of the ways that numerical information is presented in published material.

2. Statistics are presented in a range of ways, including single figures, tables, charts and graphs.

3. There are a number of reasons for presenting statistics, including to present a case, to show trends and to mislead.

In the next session we'll look at ways of using statistics to make sense of a large mass of figures.

Before you move on to Session Three, check that you have achieved the objectives given at the beginning of this session, and, if not, review the appropriate sections.

SESSION THREE

Presenting basic information

Introduction

Imagine you're at the end of a phone on a Saturday afternoon, receiving the football results as the games finish: you're dealing with large amounts of raw data. To make sense of it for the evening news it has to be categorised, ordered and presented. This session will look at the different ways of performing these tasks.

Session objectives

At the end of this session you should be able to:

- understand the importance of having a clear aim in mind when choosing the type of statistical presentation to use

- group and rearrange data in a table in order to make sense of large amounts of information

- identify ways of organising data and presenting it graphically using frequency distributions, pie charts and scattergrams

- simplify information for maximum clarity of meaning.

Defining your information requirements

One reason for using statistics is to understand large amounts of numerical information. There is a large amount of information in *Table 1*, which gives the heights and weights of 80 people.

A		B		C		D	
Height	Weight	Height	Weight	Height	Weight	Height	Weight
5.9	12.9	6.0	18.0	5.2	7.5	6.4	22.0
5.1	8.6	5.6	11.0	5.9	15.4	5.4	8.5
5.1	7.0	5.6	9.5	5.8	13.3	4.7	4.8
5.2	8.5	4.5	4.9	5.3	7.5	6.1	16.2
5.6	11.0	5.6	9.5	5.6	9.7	4.6	5.7
5.8	12.0	5.8	12.4	4.3	3.7	5.8	12.9
5.4	8.0	4.8	5.9	5.8	13.1	5.8	11.7
6.0	16.3	5.0	14.0	5.8	12.5	5.2	8.5
6.3	15.7	6.1	15.9	6.2	20.7	5.3	8.0
5.5	8.4	6.4	17.2	5.5	9.5	6.2	18.6
5.7	10.0	5.6	9.5	4.4	5.3	6.1	15.4
5.8	11.4	5.9	15.0	4.5	5.3	5.6	10.0
6.2	19.6	5.3	9.0	5.8	9.5	6.2	15.9
5.9	12.7	5.5	10.5	5.9	12.0	4.4	4.8
4.6	6.0	4.8	4.9	6.2	16.4	6.1	14.2
5.7	11.1	6.2	15.7	4.5	5.0	5.6	10.0
5.4	8.0	5.8	12.5	6.3	21.3	5.7	12.1
5.7	13.2	5.3	10.2	5.3	8.8	5.7	10.1
5.7	9.5	5.3	9.3	5.0	6.0	5.8	13.8
6.1	15.0	5.2	6.3	6.4	6.0	6.0	16.6

Table 1 Heights and weights of 80 people

Note: Heights are given in feet and tenths of a foot, so 5.5 feet in the table indicates 5 feet and 6 inches. Similarly 10.5 stones indicates 10 stone 7 pounds and 7.9 stone is 7 and nine-tenths stones, about 7 stone 12 pounds.

At first sight it's very hard to extract much information from a pageful of numbers like this, but there are ways of organising and presenting the information which can make it much easier to see what the figures show. In this session, I'll use this data to work through some of them.

Of course, the 'best' way of organising information depends on what you want to find out from it, and the questions you are interested in answering should guide the statistical presentation. (The same principle applies to the original collection of data. You may have come across this point in studying research methods.) So the place to start in dealing with this table of heights and weights is to decide on some questions: then we can go on to find ways of dealing with the numbers to help answer them.

ACTIVITY 5   ALLOW **15** MINUTES

Define the information you seek

This data contains a lot of information. Imagine you have been asked to write a summary of it to be read by the general public.

List some of the questions that might be asked by your target audience.

Here are a couple of examples:

● What is the 'normal' height and weight or 'average' height and weight of this group of people?

● Are there many particularly heavy or light people in the group?

List two or three further questions that your audience might want answered.

Commentary:

Here are the further questions which occurred to me:

● Are there any people who have an unusual combination of height and weight (or even some pairs of figures which are so unlikely that they may be mistakes)?

● Which are the tallest, shortest, lightest and heaviest people?

● Are most of the people much the same weight or are there big differences within the group?

● Is there any pattern in the relationship between height and weight? Are tall people also likely to be relatively heavy, for example? You may suspect that this would be so, but do these figures support the suspicion?

● In general, what's going on? Can you look at the numbers and give a quick summary of the interesting features of this information?

I would find it very difficult to answer these questions just by looking at the lists of figures. How can we use statistics to get information from this mass of numbers? There are two main ways of going about this. One is to transform the information into a graph or chart, and we'll try this later in this session. The other is to stick with a numerical presentation, but find ways of organising or summarising the numbers so the information is clearer. The next activity asks you to try ways of doing this.

Dealing with a large amount of data

Often by rearranging or grouping data in a table, key points can be more clearly identified or demonstrated.

ACTIVITY 6   ALLOW 15 MINUTES

Presenting the information in a more meaningful way

Try to find some ways of reordering or grouping the numbers in *Table 1* so that it is easier to see what is going on. You don't really need to rewrite the whole table as long as you're clear about what you would do.

Explain the way in which your ideas improve the presentation.

The commentary to *Activity 5* raised several questions about the data. Identify the questions that can be answered by your presentations.

Commentary:

Two kinds of improvement occur to me. The first is to change the order in which the numbers are presented. The second is to count how many people there are at each height. I'll discuss changing the order first, and give you an activity going into that in detail, and then go on to the counting approach.

I ordered the original table alphabetically by the surnames of the people measured. This produces a random-looking order for the actual figures. However, you could start with the information from the shortest people, and gradually work up to the tallest.

ACTIVITY 7

Rank ordering

Try writing out the heights and weights for the 10 shortest people below, starting with the shortest.

Commentary:

The full set of figures, ranked by height, appears as *Table 2a*. Compare it with your version.

This ranking of the data helps to answer some of the questions we started with. By looking at *Table 2a* it is now possible to identify readily the shortest and tallest heights measured, to get some idea of the overall pattern of heights, and see what values occur most frequently. For example, it's clear that 5.8 feet and 6.2 feet are both fairly common heights in the sample, whereas there happens to be no one who is 4.9 feet tall.

By looking across to see what weights are associated with the various heights, we can start to answer the 'height vs. weight' question: it does seem that taller people tend to be heavier than short people.

If you ranked the information according to weight, you could make some similar judgements about people's weights.

Height	Weight	Height	Weight
4.3	3.7	5.7	13.2
4.4	5.3	5.7	12.1
4.4	4.8	5.7	10.1
4.5	5.0	5.7	10.0
4.5	5.3	5.7	9.5
4.5	4.9	5.8	12.4
4.6	5.7	5.8	11.4
4.6	6.0	5.8	9.5
4.7	4.8	5.8	13.3
4.8	5.9	5.8	13.8
4.8	4.9	5.8	12.9
5.0	14.0	5.8	12.0
5.0	6.0	5.8	11.7
5.1	8.6	5.8	13.1
5.1	7.0	5.8	12.5
5.2	8.5	5.8	12.5
5.2	7.5	5.9	15.0
5.2	6.3	5.9	12.7
5.2	8.5	5.9	15.4
5.3	9.3	5.9	12.9
5.3	10.2	5.9	12.0
5.3	9.0	6.0	16.6
5.3	8.0	6.0	16.3
5.3	8.8	6.0	18.0
5.3	7.5	6.1	15.0
5.4	8.5	6.1	16.2
5.4	8.0	6.1	14.2
5.4	8.0	6.1	15.9
5.5	10.5	6.1	15.4
5.5	8.4	6.2	15.9
5.5	9.5	6.2	19.6
5.6	9.5	6.2	20.7
5.6	11.0	6.2	18.6
5.6	10.0	6.2	15.7
5.6	10.0	6.2	16.4
5.6	9.7	6.3	15.7
5.6	11.0	6.3	23.1
5.6	9.5	6.4	6.0
5.6	9.5	6.4	17.2
5.7	11.1	6.4	22.0

Table 2a

The other approach I mentioned was to count up the number of people there were at each height. If you wrote down a list of heights you could go through the original data, and put down a mark for each person on your list against their height. *Table 2b* summarises the heights for the people in columns A and B of *Table 1*.

Feet	Number	Feet	Number	Feet	Number
4.0		5.0	/	6.0	//
4.3		5.1	//	6.1	//
4.4		5.2	//	6.2	//
4.5	/	5.3	///	6.3	/
4.6	/	5.4	//	6.4	/
4.7		5.5	//		
4.8	//	5.6	++++		
4.9		5.7	////		
		5.8	////		
		5.9	///		

Table 2b

ACTIVITY 8   ALLOW **10** MINUTES

Building a frequency table

Use the sorted data in *Table 2a* to complete *Table 2c* below. Mark in all the heights in the relevant columns in the table and then put the final number for each height into columns R1, R2 and R3.

Feet	No.	R1	Feet	No.	R2	Feet	No.	R3
4.0			5.0	/		6.0	//	
4.3			5.1	//		6.1	//	
4.4			5.2	//		6.2	//	
4.5	/		5.3	///		6.3	/	
4.6	/		5.4	//		6.4	/	
4.7			5.5	//				
4.8	//		5.6	++++				
4.9			5.7	////				
			5.8	////				
			5.9	///				

Table 2c

Commentary:

What you have produced is called a **frequency table**. These tables are a useful quick summary, but as presented here they only tell you about one aspect of the data at a time. You could combine the information for height and weight by splitting the group of people of a certain height, say 5.6 feet, according to their weight.

*A **frequency table** is a distribution in which the number of observations at each value is counted up and then represented by a number in a table. It is the non-graphical equivalent of a frequency distribution.*

ACTIVITY 9

Extending the table

I've filled in the values for the 5.5 feet row: complete the other two rows in *Table 3*.

Height	Weight in stones							
	8.0-8.4	8.5-8.9	9.0-9.4	9.5-9.9	10.0-10.4	10.5-10.9	11.0-11.4	11.4-11.9
5.4 feet								
5.5 feet	1			1		1		
5.6 feet								

Table 3

Commentary:

You're now producing a table **crosstabulated** for height and weight. Don't worry if it took you rather more or less time than 10 minutes: people vary a lot on their speed on tasks like this. The complete table for all the groups appears as *Table 4* below.

ACTIVITY 10

Using a table to understand the data

1. Use *Table 4* to obtain figures for the following:
- particularly heavy or light people in the group
- people who have an unusual combination of height and weight (or even some pairs of figures which are so unlikely that they may be mistakes)
- the tallest, shortest, lightest and heaviest people.

2. Use *Table 4* to comment on:
- the range of heights and weights within the group
- any pattern in the relationship between height and weight: for example, are tall people also likely to be relatively heavy?

A crosstabulated table is one in which the observations are grouped into more than one category on each of two variables. A table which divided up workers according to three different grades and also according to whether they had more or less than 10 years work experience would be crosstabulated for grade and experience.

Height ft	Weight in stones									
	under 4	4-5.9	6-7.9	8-9.9	10-11.9	12-13.9	14-15.9	16-17.9	18-19.9	over 20
under 4.4	1	2								
4.5-4.9		7	1							
5.0-5.4			5	10	1		1			
5.5-5.9				8	10	13	2			
6.0-6.5			1				7	5	3	3

Table 4 Height and weight for 80 people crosstabulated

Commentary:

This table does help with several of the questions. Extreme values and unusual combinations stand out because they fall outside the area where most cells are filled. Notice that some cells are completely empty – some combinations of height and weight don't occur in our sample. The general trend of height and weight also shows up – as one increases, the other increases. The amount of detail that this presentation shows depends on the size of the divisions we choose for the cells of the table. I chose to group the information into steps of 2 stones and 0.5 feet to get the table down to a manageable size. By writing the table in this way we are beginning to move from a numerical presentation of the information to a spatial, that is graphical, presentation, and that's what we'll consider next.

Graphical presentation

For many people, representing the information with shapes and areas is clearer than using numbers. This can be done with various kinds of graphs and related figures. You will have found some examples when you did the first activity.

ACTIVITY 11 · ALLOW 10 MINUTES

Reorganising the data graphically

Refer back to the graphical methods of describing data that you identified in *Activity 3*. On a separate sheet, use two different approaches to sketch the way the height/weight data might look when represented graphically.

Commentary:

A wide range of possible presentations could be used, and a few have been sketched here in *Figure 1*.

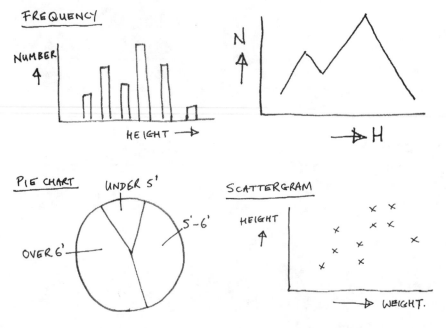

Figure 1 Possible graphical presentations of data

A frequency distribution is a distribution in which the number of observations at each value is counted up and then represented by the height of a line, bar or marker on a graph or chart.

The **frequency distribution** is really just a full graphic version of the frequency table you produced in *Activity 8*. The number of people in each category can be shown by bars (*Figure 2*) or points joined by lines (*Figure 3*).

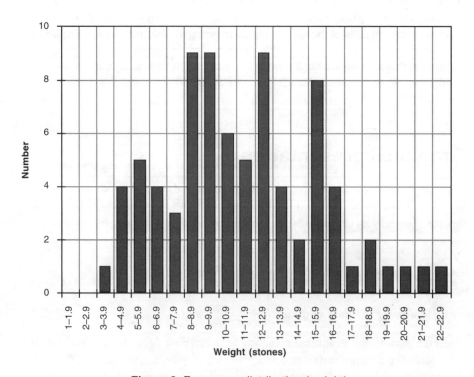

Figure 2 Frequency distribution (weight)

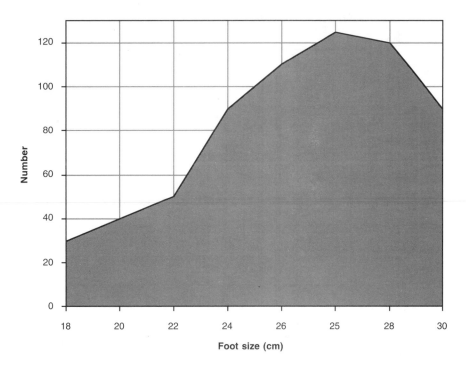

Figure 3 Frequency distribution (foot size)

A **pie chart** shows the proportion of the population that falls into each category as a sector of a disk ('a slice of a pie'). The angle of the sector is proportional to the relative size of the group represented. As just under 24% of the group were over 6 feet they can be represented by 24% of the perimeter of a circle (which is just under 90° on the pie chart). Those between 5 and 5.4 feet were about 20% of the group and they are shown as about 20% (one fifth) of the circle or a sector of about 72°. The remaining groups are represented similarly.

*A **pie chart** is a graphic representation of data in which the proportions of observations falling into different categories are shown as different-sized sectors of a circle (or slices of a pie).*

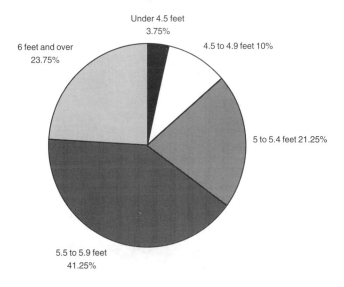

Figure 4 Pie chart (height)

One way of combining information about height and weight measures in one graphic is to use a **scattergram** in which every observation (every person for this example) is shown by one point in the graphic. The horizontal position of that point is governed by the person's weight and the vertical position of the point is governed by the person's height. So the points representing two people, one for a person 11 stone in weight and 5.5 feet in height, and the second for a person 14 stone in weight and 5 feet tall, would look like the scattergram in *Figure 5*.

A **scattergram** *is a graphic in which the relationship between sets of measures on two variables is displayed by plotting each observation on a graph with one of the variables as the horizontal axis, and the other variable as the vertical axis. This produces a pattern of markers – one marker for each observation – from which any pattern in the relationship may be seen.*

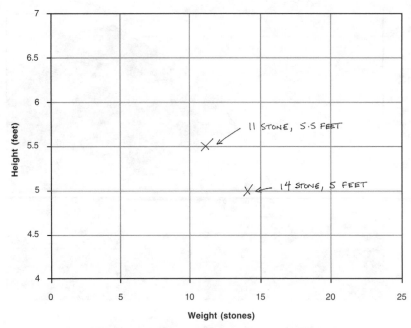

Figure 5 Scattergram of height and weight

Plotting the points for all the people in our sample gives a scattergram as in *Figure 6*.

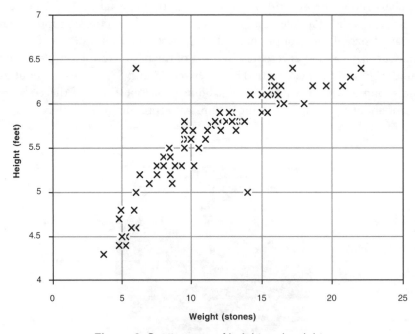

Figure 6 Scattergram of height and weight

ACTIVITY 12 ALLOW 25 MINUTES

Using graphical presentation

In statistics the most appropriate presentations are related to what you might want to find out about a set of figures.

To start this activity let's go back to some of the questions that came out of *Activity 10*. You might want information on:

a)   The overall pattern of heights and weights
b)   The range
c)   Common values

d)   The midpoint
e)   Any unusual values/groups
f)   Proportions falling into different classes of value
g)   The relationship between height and weight
h)   Unusual combinations of values

Look at each of the three presentations in *Figures 2, 4* and *6*. Using a tick
(✓), a cross (✗) and where necessary a comment, indicate in the table below
whether each type of figure shows the information requested in a) to h).

	Frequency distribution	Pie chart	Scattergram
a) The overall pattern of heights and weights			
b) The range			
c) Common values			
d) The midpoint			
e) Any unusual values/groups			
f) Proportions falling into different classes of value			
g) The relationship between height and weight			
h) Unusual combinations of values			

Commentary:

Below is my completed table and comments. Your table should be similar, although you may well have chosen different items for comment.

	Frequency distribution	Pie chart	Scattergram
a) The overall pattern of heights and weights	✓	✓	✓
b) The range	✓ Most people are between 5 and 17 stones	✗	✓
c) Common values	Appear as peaks	✓ But very roughly	✓ Where the points are most dense
d) The midpoint	✗ The centre of gravity of the chart, but not easy to find here	✗	✓
e) Any unusual values/groups	✓ Easy to find those who are unusually heavy	✗	✓ Where single points stand by themselves such as the light but tall person and the heavy but short person
f) Proportions falling into different classes of value	✓	✓ But only for the categories chosen – what about 5.6 feet to 5.8 feet?	✓ Just draw a line from a weight or height and count the crosses
g) The relationship between height and weight	✗ No information on the relationship at all	✗ No information on the relationship at all	✓
h) Unusual combinations of values	✗	✗	✓ Where single points stand by themselves and the points at the extremes

More complicated figures

What if there were more dimensions of information than just height and weight? It is possible to construct 'three-dimensional' graphs which pack in even more information. *Figure 7* below shows a series of weight frequency distributions for different heights.

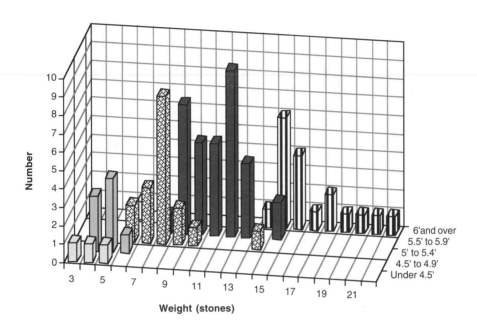

Figure 7 Frequency distributions (separated by height)

Many computer programs for handling numbers can produce figures like these easily, and the temptation is to cram everything in. This is a mistake. The figure shown here is so complicated that it is difficult to decipher: the best guide is to go back to the kind of questions from *Activity 9* that you have been considering over the last few pages. What is your message? Once you've decided that, you can choose a figure that gives that information simply and straightforwardly.

Summary

1. In this session we have examined the need for organising and simplifying a large amount of data to make it easier to understand.

2. It is important to have a clear aim in mind when choosing the type of statistical presentation to use.

3. We examined ranking, frequency tables, frequency distributions, pie charts and scattergrams.

4. We also examined more complicated presentations. I pointed out that you should try to ensure that the complexity doesn't obscure the information you want.

Before you move on to Session Four, check that you have achieved the objectives given at the beginning of this session, and, if not, review the appropriate sections.

Summarising and simplifying data

Introduction

This session is about ways of summing up a mass of data in one or two numbers. I'll introduce different kinds of 'average' and discuss their advantages and drawbacks. I'll also mention other measures based on the range and spread of the data.

Session objectives

At the end of this session you should be able to:

- describe three main measures of central tendency – the mean, the mode and the median

- explain the ways in which these measures are affected by changes in the data

- select the most appropriate measure for particular purposes.

The mean, the mode and the median

Often it's useful to sum up a large amount of information in a few words or numbers and I have tried to show that this is one of the reasons for using statistics. The next activity provides an extreme version of this: reducing 80 measurements to just one statistic.

ACTIVITY 13　　　　　　　ALLOW **10** MINUTES

Summing it all up with one number

Look back at the height and weight figures in *Table 2a*, page 22.

● Pick out or calculate a single value which sums up all the information about the heights of the people in this sample.

● Suggest one or two alternatives that you could have used.

Commentary:

Don't worry if you had difficulty finding an answer you consider to be entirely satisfactory. There is no obvious answer because it isn't really possible to reduce a mass of information to just one figure in a satisfactory manner. The one most people think of first is usually called the 'average', more properly called the mean. You may have thought of other measures, based on the most common value or some kind of value that's 'in the middle'. We will discuss versions of these later in this session.

So, what is the mean height of all these people? It works out at 5.6 feet, or about 5 feet 7 inches, and it's calculated by adding all of their heights together and then dividing by the number of people (there are 80 people in the table and their heights added together come to 448 feet; divide by 80 to give a mean of 5.6).

This seems pretty good. Even though we know that there are lots of people in our sample whose heights are quite different from the mean, 5.6 feet, or 5 feet 7 inches, seems quite reasonable as a 'normal' or 'representative' height.

But what if we do the same calculation for weight? This gives a mean weight of 11.2 stone. That's perfectly correct as the mean, but it doesn't *seem* as representative of the group to me – it seems a bit heavy. What has made the difference?

Although people in our sample vary quite a bit in height, there is no one who is 12 feet tall – not surprisingly. However with the weight figures, there are a group of people who are *very much* heavier than most of the others. When their weights are added in with everyone else's when working out the mean, they have a disproportionate effect. So the final mean is biased by their extreme values.

ACTIVITY 14   ALLOW 10 MINUTES

Biasing the mean

A unit is staffed by 10 nurses, earning the salaries set out below.

£10,000 £10,000 £10,000 £10,000 £11,000 £13,000 £13,000 £14,000 £14,000 £15,000

Calculate their mean salary.

Add the salaries of two consultants to this group, each being paid £50,000, and again calculate the mean salary of the unit's staff. Comment on the effect of adding the consultants' pay.

An average, *in statistical terms, is any way of calculating a middle or representative value that can stand for a set of figures – and there are several ways of doing this. The technical term is* **measures of central tendency.** *Some of them, the mean, median and mode, will be discussed in this session. The kind of average most commonly thought of, where you add up all the values and divide by the number of cases, is called the* **mean.** *That's the term I'll use from now on. The problem of representing the variability in a set of figures (the weights of a group of people are much more variable than their heights, for example) will be discussed in Session Six, when we consider statistics like standard deviation.*

Commentary:

In the first case, the total salary is £120,000. Divide that by 10 (the number of people) to get the mean: £12,000.

If the group includes the consultants, the total is now £220,000; divide by 12 (the new number of people) to get the mean: £18,333 approximately.

There are two points worth noting here: firstly, a mean value may not actually correspond with anyone in the group it describes, and second, a few extreme values can bias the mean quite a lot.

ACTIVITY 15 ALLOW 15 MINUTES

Unrepresentative means

Here are a couple of means for you to consider which don't seem very representative.

Estimate the mean number of testicles (or if you prefer it, the mean number of ovaries) for people in the UK.

Estimate the mean number of children in UK families.

Commentary:

For the first, you know that more than half the population (the females) have no testicles, and in the rest of the population, two is very common with higher and lower numbers quite rare, so a reasonable estimate would be a bit less than one – let's say 0.95. The mean number of ovaries might be slightly greater than one – perhaps 1.05.

Most people have heard the statement that 'the average family has 2.4 children'. This is more folklore than statistics, and anyway, since many families are the result of divorce and remarriage, it's difficult to define 'a family' to allow you to do the calculations, but let's accept 2.4 for the sake of the argument.

Both these values (0.95 testicles/1.05 ovaries and 2.4 children) seem unsatisfactory. You are unlikely to come across any person or any family which match them.

In the first case, the problem arises because you've combined two groups which aren't comparable. Although both males and females are people, only males have testicles, only females have ovaries, so asking for a value for 'people' rather than specifying the relevant sex wasn't very sensible. It was a silly question in the first place.

An example that is less obviously silly is combining figures from other very different groups. Mean wages of management and workers combined may be different from the usual pay of either group.

The problem with the '2.4 children' is different. It seems sensible to combine figures from families and then work out a mean, but the result is an impossibility for any one family. Statistics are abstract representations, after all, so they don't have to correspond to any concrete case. Perhaps it means that families with two children or with three children are both quite common. (In the session on the mode, below, we will discuss using common values, rather than the mean, to represent a group.)

This figure for mean number of children isn't useless, by any means. For instance, to decide what paediatric provision was needed for families moving into a new estate, you might want to know the mean number of children under 10 for households likely to move in. So if you knew that mean was 2.3, say, rather than 1.9, it would lead to different decisions about demand even though the most common number of children per household might be two in both cases and no household would actually have 2.3 – or 1.9 – children.

Statistics other than the mean

In *Activity 13* we tried to find a single number that summed up all the information about the heights of people in a particular group. Having decided that it was an impossible task we settled for the mean as next best thing. Now its time to discuss other possible statistics besides the mean.

Another measure that might have occurred to you is to try to find the 'middle' of the set of figures in a more direct way than calculating the mean. What is the height midway between the tallest person and the shortest? What is the height of the person who has half the group taller than them and half shorter?

These two measures are similar in their basic idea but different in the amount they are used, and in their usefulness. The first is the **mid-point of the range** and is not a commonly used statistic. The second (the halfway point in the rankings) is the **median** and is a powerful and important statistic.

*The **mid-point of the range** is the value in a set of observations which lies midway between the highest value and the lowest. Often confused with the median, which is the mid-point of the rankings, and quite different. The mid-point of the range is not a very useful statistic. The **median** is the value that divides the rankings of all the observed cases in half, so that half the values are higher and half lower.*

ACTIVITY 16

Using the mid-point to represent the group

● What is the problem of using the mid-point of the range to represent the whole group?

● Can you think of cases when it would not represent the group well?

● Are there any similar problems with the median?

Commentary:

The difficulty with the mid-point of the range is that it's very strongly affected by whatever happen to be the greatest and smallest values. If a 7 feet tall basketball player were added to the data for height, the mid-point of the height range would change quite a bit. Thinking about the effects that changing the data might have on the various measures of central tendency is quite a powerful way of working out their usefulness.

The median, on the other hand, is quite unaffected by bringing in a few extreme values to expand the range: in fact it's not affected by *whatever* happens at the top and bottom of the set of values. It only depends on the rankings, and whatever value is at the mid-point of the rankings. This is both a weakness and a strength. The median height for this group is 5.7 feet, slightly higher than the mean.

ACTIVITY 17

Another way of representing the group

Look at the frequency distribution of heights noted in Session Three. It's reproduced below (*Figure 8*), with the mean and median values shown as well. Is there any other kind of 'common' or 'ordinary' value apparent from this figure that you could use to represent the group? (Hint: there may be more than one 'common' value here.)

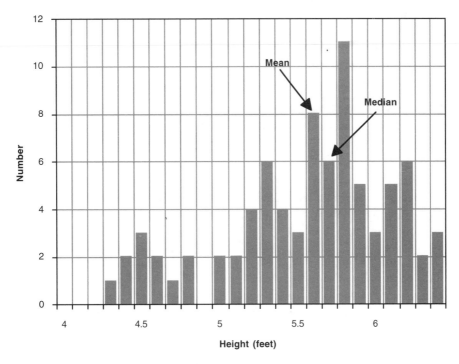

Figure 8 Frequency distribution (height)

Commentary:

You could pick on the 'humps' in this distribution. They are the most common values, after all. They are called modes, and the main mode is at 5.8 feet because there are more people at this height than at any other. There are other 'humps' at 5.3 feet and 6.2 feet: but they are not the most common values overall, although they are quite common among the smaller and taller people in the group.

When there is more than one hump in a distribution it's often a sign that there are values from rather different groups lumped together in the same set of data. In this case, you may already have guessed that the sampled population is made up of more than one group. **Bimodal** and **multimodal** distributions like this will be discussed in Session Five.

*The **mode** is a measure of central tendency. The mode is the most common value among a set of observations. It is possible for there to be more than one mode for any set of figures. Other measures of central tendency are the mean and the median.*

The measure based on the most common value (properly called the **mode**) has its drawbacks. All it needs is for a few values to gather together and they will appear as a mode, no matter what all the other values are. You might think a measure like this doesn't have much practical significance, but it's important in our lives in at least one area – the British political system. The mode is used to decide the winner in parliamentary elections: it's the candidate who gets the largest number of votes who wins, no matter how many votes are spread amongst the other candidates. The modal choice triumphs. This has the interesting consequence that most governments are elected by a minority of the electorate: the majority has split its vote amongst various rival parties. It's one area where people demonstrate their practical understanding of statistics quite well: splitting the vote and tactical voting are (statistically speaking) devices intended to manipulate the mode – and most people know how to go about that if they want to.

ACTIVITY 18　　ALLOW **10** MINUTES

More paradoxical averages

Suppose you read that the life expectancy at birth varies widely from century to century and from country to country. The figures given are 73 for Britain in the 1980s, 47 for England in the seventeenth century, and 54 for Bolivia in 1990.

On the other hand, it's been said for centuries that 'the years of men are three score and ten' (the 'years of women' might have varied rather more). This statement was taken to be generally true even when life expectancy was much lower than seventy years. Why do you think that this is the case?

Commentary:

It depends what statistic is used for the 'life expectancy' figure. If the mean is used then we know that it can be distorted by extreme values: a few people who lived for hundreds of years would inflate the mean. What is more likely is that people who live for a very short length of time affect the mean by pulling it down. High levels of infant mortality will affect the mean life expectancy at birth very strongly. A life expectancy of 35 probably doesn't mean that many people die in their thirties: it probably means that the numbers of people who die late in life are balanced by large numbers of people who die very young. A 35-year-old in such a society might have quite a good chance of living till old age. You can see some evidence of this by looking at mean life expectancies at different ages: the remaining life expectancies for adults in different societies are often much closer to each other than the life expectancies at birth in those societies.

Choosing the most appropriate measure

Now that you've been introduced to these three measures of central tendency, and discussed some of their strengths and weaknesses, it's time to consider how they might be used in a particular case.

ACTIVITY 19	ALLOW 15 MINUTES

Choosing between different measures of central tendency

Below is a table and a graph (*Figure 9*) giving details of survival times of patients after the onset of some illness. These figures are invented, but they're not very different from those given for survival after heart attacks. Identify which of the three measures of central tendency (mean, median or mode) best summarises these figures.

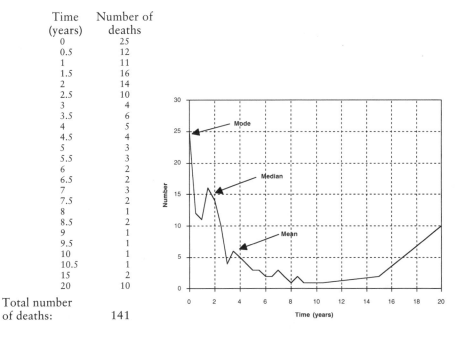

Time (years)	Number of deaths
0	25
0.5	12
1	11
1.5	16
2	14
2.5	10
3	4
3.5	6
4	5
4.5	4
5	3
5.5	3
6	2
6.5	2
7	3
7.5	2
8	1
8.5	2
9	1
9.5	1
10	1
10.5	1
15	2
20	10
Total number of deaths:	141

Figure 9 Survival time (years) after onset of illness (number of people dying each time)

Commentary:

None of them are a particularly good overall summary. Perhaps it depends on why you want to summarise. Let me put the question again in a more helpful form.

ACTIVITY 20   ALLOW **15** MINUTES

Choosing a measure to suit a purpose

We have identified three measures: mode, mean and median.

Select the measure that would most appropriately satisfy information needs if:

a) you are a health service manager who wants to decide where to invest resources to give you a chance of saving as many lives as possible

b) you are a counsellor who wants to give people (sufferers or potential sufferers) honest information about survival chances

c) you are an accountant who wants to predict the long-term costs of providing treatment to all sufferers from this disease in the whole country.

Commentary:

a) If you're investing resources, perhaps you want to help as large a number of people as possible. Perhaps investing in emergency and short-term care (if there's some effective treatment) would pay off because the largest number of people (the mode) die very soon after onset. The mode seems a useful measure to use in trying to decide here.

b) In advising people on their survival chances, neither the mode (affected by the high 'instant mortality' rate but not representative of 80% of sufferers), nor the mean (biased by the few people with very long survival times) seems helpful. The median is the point at which half the sufferers have survived, half died: it seems a good '50/50' or 'evens chance' figure to give people. This is complicated a little because if you were counselling survivors, the group of people who die at onset wouldn't really be relevant. The median survival time for the group who don't die straight away is longer than that for the whole group of sufferers.

c) To make general predictions for large groups of people, a measure which uses as much as possible of the information might be appropriate. The few people who survive for a very long time do bias the mean, and they aren't very typical, but they do make a difference to the pattern of deaths. They might make a big difference to the overall cost of providing care to sufferers in this population. In this case, the mean, which includes all the available information, might be a useful statistic.

These three statistics are all fairly crude. In the real world, people try to develop more complicated, but more sensitive and appropriate, measures to fit particular cases. Here a measure of QALYs, Quality Adjusted Life Years gained, might be useful, especially for (c).

It might still seem to you that none of these measures by itself would be enough, or appropriate. I think that's right: measures of general tendency (indeed most statistics) provide a crude summary of the original information. They are economical and useful, but it's often necessary to look at several statistics, or to go back to the original information, to get the fuller picture.

So far I've discussed the **range** as a way of representing the data, and suggested that it was of limited usefulness because it was affected by any extreme values. All the same, the idea of representing the amount of variation in the figures is important. After all, a group of people with mean height five feet six inches who are all between five feet three inches and five feet nine inches is very different from a group of people with the same mean height, but with individual heights varying from three feet to seven feet. The difference between these two groups would show up on a frequency distribution. Distributions can show quite a lot about the patterns in a set of numbers and the next session will discuss using frequency distributions (and numerical statistics related to them) as one way of getting a fuller picture.

*The **range** is the measure which is the difference between the largest observed value and the smallest, a fairly crude statistic.*

Summary

1. You should now be able to describe the three common measures of central tendency, the mean, the median and the mode and be aware of the pitfalls of each.

2. The mean can be biased by a few extreme values and may not represent any particular measures in a group, especially when different subgroups are lumped together.

3. The median is less affected by unusual values than the mean.

4. The mode will be affected if a few values are gathered together, no matter what the other values are.

5. The three measures discussed all have advantages and drawbacks. It is important to consider the purpose of using the statistic in deciding which might be most useful.

Before you move on to Session Five, check that you have achieved the objectives given at the beginning of this session, and, if not, review the appropriate sections.

Distributions

Introduction

Session Three introduced the use of frequency distributions as a way of summarising and presenting height and weight data (*Activity 11*). This session will examine distributions in more detail, look at how they might be interpreted and explain some new statistical measures related to distributions. To start with you'll build up a distribution based on a series of chance events, and record the process so you can see the way in which the pattern changes as more observations are added.

Session objectives

At the end of this session you should be able to:

- use frequency distributions for summarising and presenting data

- appreciate that the shape of a distribution is determined by the processes giving rise to it

- describe typical deviations from ideal forms, such as skewedness, humps and dips, and be able to suggest reasons for them.

Using a frequency distribution to present data

ACTIVITY 21   ALLOW **20** MINUTES

A frequency distribution based on chance

Use the prepared graph below (*Figure 10*).

Toss a coin 10 times and note how many times it comes down heads. Fill in a square in the appropriate column on the graph. For instance if you get 6 heads, fill in the square just above the '6' on the bottom axis.

Toss the coin another 10 times, counting how many heads you get. Fill in the appropriate square on the graph again. Carry on doing this for another 13 sets of coin tosses, making 15 in all. If you get the same number of heads as on a previous set of 10 tosses, fill in the square above the one you previously filled in for that number.

Do another 15 sets of 10 coin tosses, but this time use a pen of a different colour to fill in the results on the graph. Finish off with a final 15 sets of tosses, using a different pen again. A total of 45 sets of coin tosses should be enough to make the point without exhausting your patience.

Comment on the way in which the graphs change their shape and propose a reason for the change.

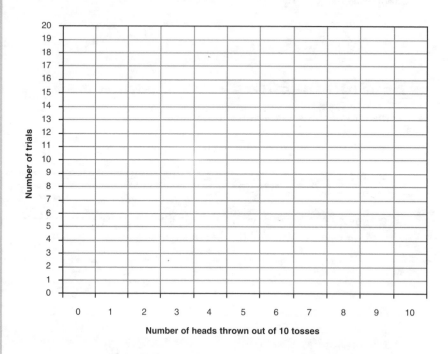

Figure 10 Frequency distribution: random coin toss

Commentary:

Since this activity is based on a random process the outcome can't be predicted exactly although it is possible to predict a likely outcome. The distribution for the first 15 trials probably doesn't show much pattern, but as you successively record more and more trials the distribution is likely to become more regular. *Figure 11* shows sets of results for the activity.

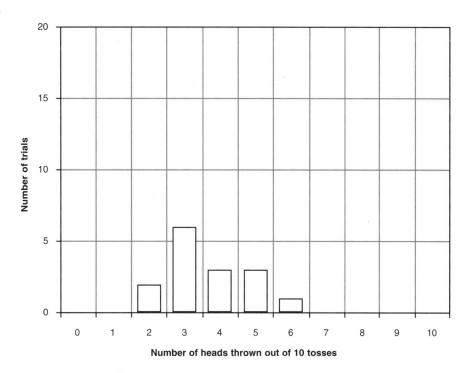

Figure 11a Frequency distribution: random coin toss (15 sets of 10 tosses)

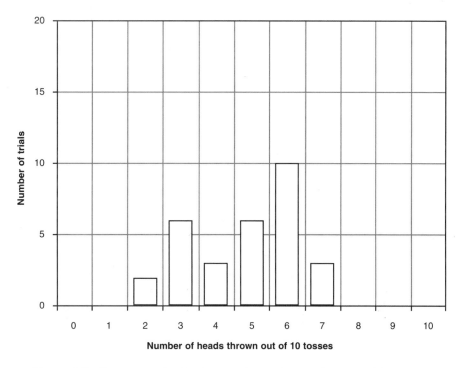

Figure 11b Frequency distribution: random coin toss (30 sets of 10 tosses)

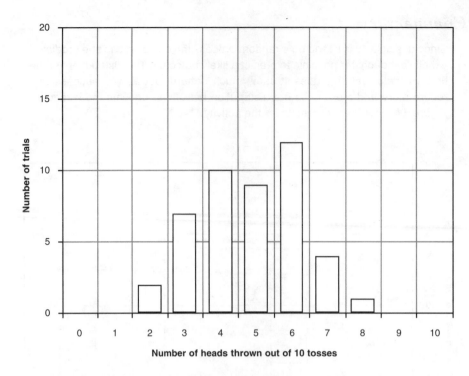

Figure 11c Frequency distribution: random coin toss (45 sets of 10 tosses)

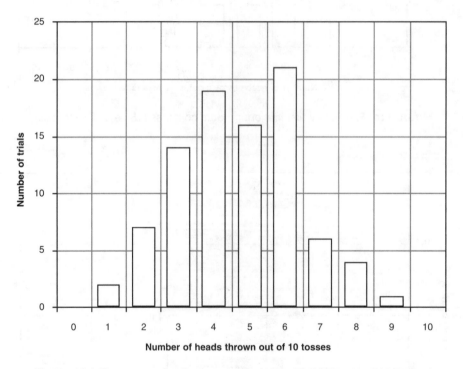

Figure 11d Frequency distribution: random coin toss (90 sets of 10 tosses)

The pattern for a large number of sets of tosses is quite smooth and regular. Most observations are of 4, 5 or 6 heads out of 10 with other values increasingly rare as they get nearer to 10 heads or zero heads (10 tails) in a row. This kind of frequency distribution is often described as being a bell-shaped curve, and it's typical of distributions produced by combining a large number of chance events.

The pattern you've produced might be interesting and useful to a coin-tossing enthusiast, but what does it have to do with everyday life, or health-related statistics? The next activity will try to make that connection.

ACTIVITY 22

Chance distributions in everyday life

The patterns I've been discussing are produced by the combination of a large number of random effects.

For this activity, write down some sets of statistics of interest to you which are noticeably influenced by collections of random events. I say 'noticeably influenced' because there are few processes that are totally random.

Commentary:

Just as there are few things completely random, there are few areas of life where chance doesn't play some part, so there is a wide range of possible answers here. You may have thought of chance variations in income, weather, marriage partners, exam results: the list is probably endless.

One area is the topic we've been discussing in the earlier sessions: people's physical measurements. Height and weight are partly affected by inheritance, partly by environment. The hereditary effects are probably produced by a number of genes, randomly shuffled in reproduction, and many of the environmental effects are fairly random, so it's not surprising that records of the heights of people in large populations show the bell-shaped form mentioned earlier.

Statistics on accidents and disease morbidity may also show this pattern. One of our ideas about an 'accident' is that it has a large random component (otherwise we might call it a 'certainty'). The *chances* (notice that it's quite natural to use the word here) of surviving a disease may depend on access to treatment, quality of treatment, pre-existing physical factors, even time of year – and all of these may apply fairly randomly to sufferers.

Interpreting different patterns

It's quite fair to object that none of the examples used so far is entirely governed by chance. The fact that I've always been heavier than my brother may be largely to do with random genetic variation: the fact that we've both got much heavier over the last few years is probably a non-random product of the changes in metabolism and lifestyle that come with middle age. Again, chance *may* help people to pass exams, but it helps best those who are best prepared. Morbidity can be systematically affected by variations in lifestyle: smoking and lung disease, for example. But knowledge of chance patterns can help us in detecting these non-chance processes: *deviations* from the ideal bell-shaped curve can alert us to non-chance factors operating on the population.

Similarly, other kinds of process will produce characteristic distributions. This can be illustrated with some imagined distributions for age at death. Suppose the chances of dying were exactly the same, whatever age you were: a 60-year-old would be just as likely to die in the next year as a 10-year-old. This pattern probably applies to simple organisms like bacteria and would produce an age-at-death distribution such as the one shown in *Figure 12*.

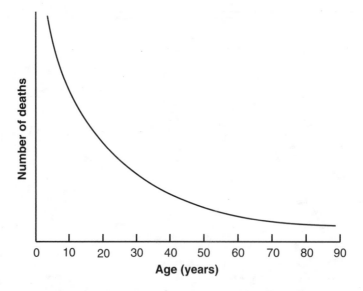

Figure 12 Frequency distribution of age at death

If there was a standard life span (perhaps the 70 years discussed in *Activity 18*) the distribution would be like the one shown in *Figure 13*.

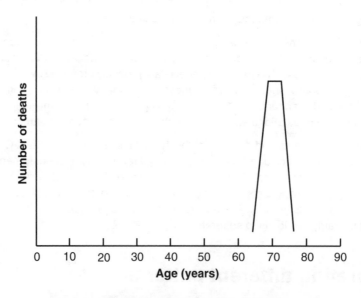

Figure 13 Frequency distribution of age at death

This is what we might expect for the time-to-failure distribution of carefully made components – light bulbs for example. Of course, random variation in manufacture and conditions of use creeps in, even for light bulbs, so the real pattern might be more like the one in *Figure 14*.

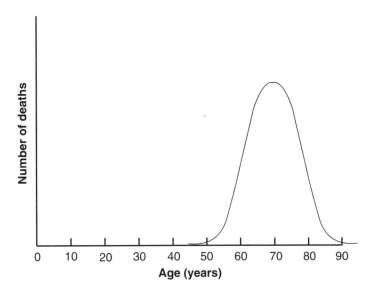

Figure 14 Frequency distribution of age at death

The bell shape shows random variation about the mean of 70. The more variable the product and the conditions of use the wider that variation will be. The issue of variation and the 'spread' of the distribution will be discussed in more detail in *Session Six* of this unit.

Now you have seen some 'ideal' patterns, we should look at a 'real-world' one. The next activity asks you to interpret the overall pattern, to look for deviations from the ideal, and to make some guesses about what those deviations might mean.

ACTIVITY 23   ALLOW **10** MINUTES

Interpreting a distribution

Figure 15 is a frequency distribution showing the number of people dying at different ages in a population. Describe the graph in terms of human behaviour and lifestyle. Are we more like bacteria or light bulbs?

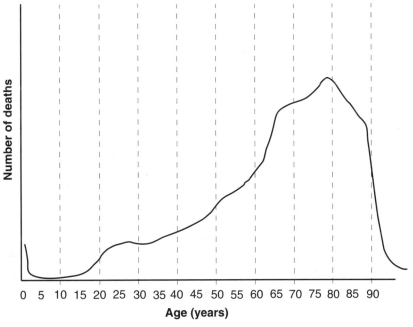

Figure 15 Frequency distribution of age at death for males

Commentary:

As far as lifespan goes, we're more like light bulbs than bacteria. There is a definite peak at 75, and some sign of random variation about that peak. But the spread of age at death is much greater than in the 'light bulb' case.

ACTIVITY 24

ALLOW 10 MINUTES

Further interpretation

Consider the deviations from the main pattern in the distribution in *Figure 15*. This isn't a regular, symmetrical curve.

● Mark the points where the curve seems irregular.

● List two or three guesses about what might have caused the irregularities.

Commentary:

I've marked on the graph below what seem to me to be the variations, with guesses about what they represent. However, it's important to stress that these are guesses.

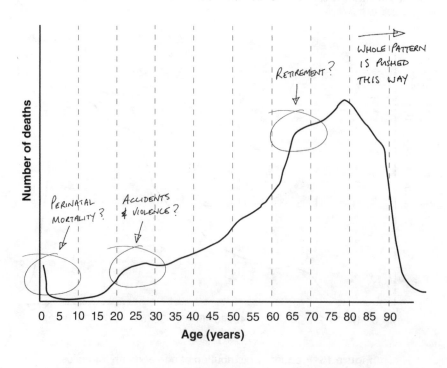

Figure 16 Frequency distribution of age at death for males

This kind of statistical survey doesn't *prove* anything. For a start, the variations from the 'ideal' could be just chance – you probably saw plenty of irregular results when you did the random coin tossing. **Inferential statistics** are designed to help distinguish 'chance' events from 'real' ones, and even when we're fairly sure that there is a non-chance variation, it would take different kinds of research to *establish* what the cause would be. The kind of analysis you've done is valuable for arousing suspicions, forming hypotheses and stimulating research, but not valid as a way of proving a case.

Inferential statistics are that part of statistics concerned with establishing whether data provides a basis for making inferences or predictions about what is likely to happen in other cases. This is in contrast with descriptive statistics, which are concerned with describing and representing data for the case at hand.

Skewed distributions

There are two kinds of distortion of the simple bell-shaped curve in *Figure 16*. There are bumps and hollows, where the numbers are locally higher or lower than might be expected, but there is an *overall distortion* of the pattern. It is pushed or twisted – statisticians say **skewed** – towards one end of the range or the other. In this case the main peak is pushed over to the right. Many more people die old than young, but there isn't a long tail of people who die at 120, 140 or 150 years to balance those who die at 30, 20 or in infancy. This pattern is called **negative skew**. Other everyday distributions are skewed in the opposite direction. *Figure 17* shows a **positively skewed** frequency distribution of income for people in work. The people represented by area A get rather little compared with a sizeable minority, area B, who earn much more.

*The **skew** is the extent to which a distribution is biased towards one end or other of the range of observations. The symmetrical normal distribution has no skew. A positively skewed distribution has most values towards the lower end of the range of observations. In a frequency distribution, the shape is biased to the left.*

A negatively skewed distribution has most values towards the higher end of the range of observations. In a frequency distribution, the shape is biased to the right.

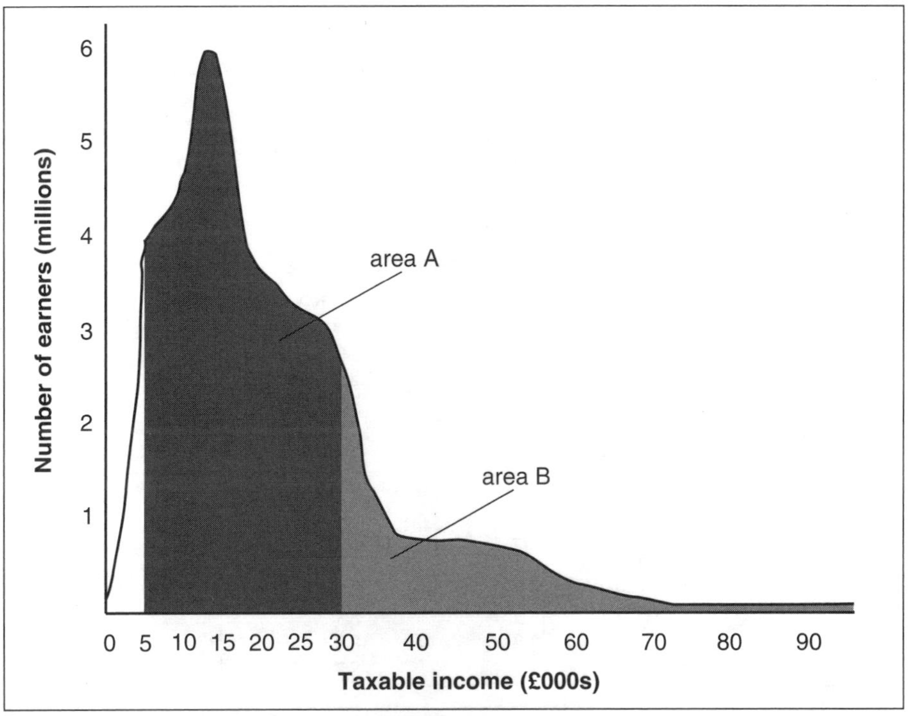

Figure 17 Taxable income in the UK 1991-92
(roughly based on Social Trends 22)

This may be a result of social processes and choices, but there is another rather basic factor that makes a skewed pattern likely: there is a lower limit to how much you can earn, but not much sign of an upper limit. The long tail of people making 1, 5, 10 or more million pounds a year is not balanced by people making several millions less than zero.

This skewedness is a feature of many natural distributions. Basic inequalities and fairly fixed upper or lower limits are fairly common, after all. One important consequence of skew in a distribution is the effect it has on the measures of central tendency. The next activity gives you a chance to explore this effect.

ACTIVITY 25 — ALLOW FIVE MINUTES

Skew and measures of central tendency

Here is a simple distribution which is heavily skewed. *Table 5a* gives the original values from which the distribution was constructed; *Table 5b* gives the interval and cumulative frequencies for the data.

Determine the mean, median and mode for the distribution.

Original figures

85	5	13	16	16
90	7	15	12	15
95	10	16	14	20
101	14	22	7	25
5	15	26	6	7
11	17	33	2	6
16	20	37	0	13
6	26	41	6	12
8	31	47	6	15
13	36	51	12	15
16	42	57	10	20
102	46	62	16	7
96	53	65	15	6
91	56	73	21	11
87	62	91	26	16
81	65	69	32	23
76	71	45	36	8
1	77	37	4	6
5	80	30	5	12
8	18	27	7	15
12	10	24	11	21
Sum of all the numbers				3200

Table 5a

Frequency tables

Interval	Number in data	Cumulative number in data:
0–4	4	4
5–9	19	23
10–14	16	39
15–19	16	55
20–24	8	63
25–29	5	68
30–34	4	72
35–39	4	76
40–44	2	78
45–49	3	81
50–54	2	83
55–59	2	85
60–64	2	87
65–69	3	90
70–74	2	92
75–79	2	94
80–84	2	96
85–89	2	98
90–94	3	101
95–99	2	103
100–104	2	105

Table 5b

Commentary:

When the distribution is symmetrical the mean, median and mode work out the same, but for a skewed distribution they can be markedly different: the mean and median are shifted towards the longer 'tail' and the longer the 'tail' is the more the mean shifts away from the mode. Having an idea of the overall shape of the distribution can be useful in choosing which of the three measures of central tendency to use in representing the data. *Figure 18* shows the graph with the values labelled.

The mean is approximately 30.47. (There are 105 numbers; the sum of all numbers is 3,200; therefore the mean equals 3,200 divided by 105.)

The median value falls within the band 15–19. (There are 105 numbers; therefore the median value will be the 53rd number when ranked in order [the half-way point in the rankings]; the final column in Table 5b shows that this occurs in the band 15–19.)

The most common value – the mode – is the band 5–9 with 15 observations.

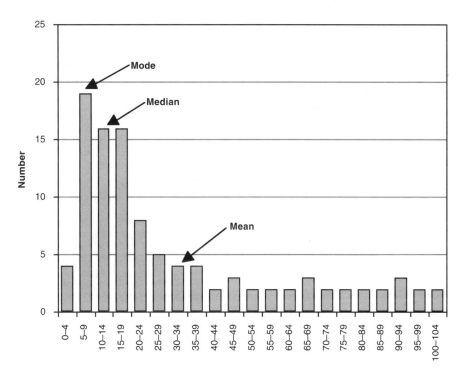

Figure 18 Frequency distribution

Single-mode and multimodal distributions

All the distributions we've examined so far in this session have had one main 'hump'. Although there may be minor irregularities and the distribution may be skewed, it's pretty clear where the middle of the distribution is. The next activity is about spotting and interpreting a different kind of pattern in distributions.

ACTIVITY 26

Large irregularities in distributions

Refer back to the distribution of weights in *Figure 2* on page 26.

How many 'main humps' can you spot in the distribution?

Suggest a reason for the appearance of different peaks at different parts of the distribution in this collection of information about people's weights

Commentary:

The distribution, like most collections of figures about real people, has a number of irregularities, but there are peaks at 5–5.9 stones, between 8 and 9.9 stones, at 12–12.9 stones, and at 15–15.9 stones.

What do these peaks mean in terms of what they represent about the original figures? They mean that there were relatively large numbers of people at these various weights. The modal weight for the whole distribution is actually 9.5 stones, the most common value overall. If you look back to *Table 2*, you will see that six values of 9.5 were recorded, more than any other value. There are relatively fewer people who have weights in the ranges 7–7.9, 11–11.9 or 14–14.9 stones, these correspond to the dips between peaks.

These are the common values, and if you look at the weights near to those peaks, you'll see that they are fairly common too. There are relatively fewer people who have weights of 6.5, 7 or 14.5 stones: these correspond to the dips in between the peaks.

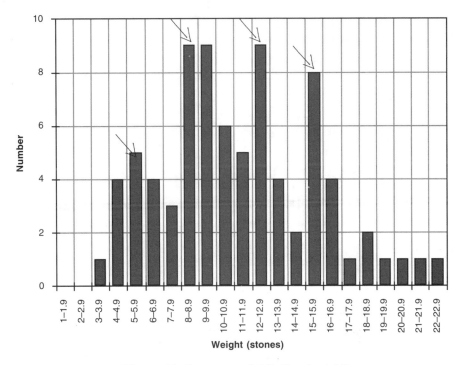

Figure 19 Frequency distribution (weight)

What could be the explanation for a pattern like this? You might decide it's just a matter of chance variation. After all, the patterns you got when you did the coin-tossing exercise probably showed a variety of peaks and valleys which appeared and disappeared as you did more trials. In this case, though, a more systematic explanation might have occurred to you. There could be some different kinds of people here – that is, some groups that have rather different characteristics. One group is rather light, one group seems quite ordinary (modal weight of 9.5 stones), and the third is rather heavy, with several people between 15 and 16 stones, and a heaviest member of 23.5 stones. You might already have guessed what kind of people are represented in the three groups. One was children, the second college students (mainly women), the third male American football and baseball players. You couldn't tell all that just from the figures, of course, but any guess about a group of smaller people, one of everyday size people, and a third group artificially selected to be particularly heavy, is a reasonable reflection of the data. This does not fully explain the large number of people weighing 12–12.9 stone. I think this is an overlap between the heavier college students and the lighter athletes.

As you might have guessed from the title of this part of the session, distributions like the one I've been discussing are called **multimodal** distributions, whereas the single-humped kind is **unimodal**. A two-humped distribution is called **bimodal**. Multimodal distributions are often produced when figures from more than one group are combined. A multimodal distribution gets its name because it has multiple modes. Usually, there is only one overall mode, but the humps can be seen as 'local modes'.

The graphs in *Figure 20* represent three distributions for different groups.

*A **unimodal** distribution has a single mode. The frequency distribution will show one main hump.*

*A **bimodal** distribution has two modes; that is, two values that are the most common values in the distribution. The two values need not be exactly the same, so only one of them will actually be the mode for the set of observations.*

*A **multimodal** distribution has several modes; that is, more than one value that is the most common value in the distribution. These values need not be exactly the same, so only one of them will actually be the mode for the set of observations. As long as a distribution shows several distinct humps, it can be described as multimodal.*

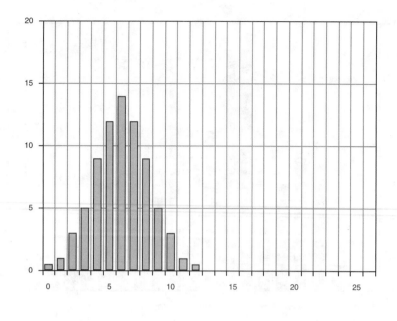

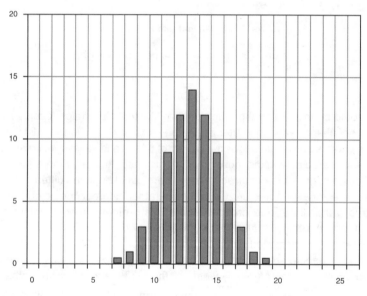

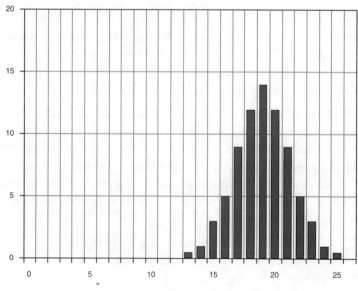

Figure 20

If they are added together they give:

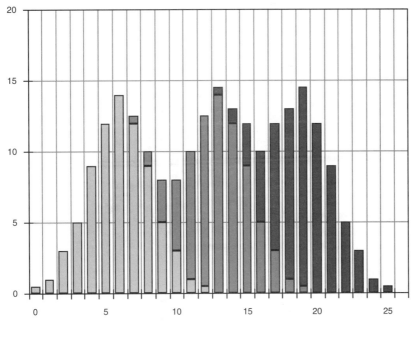

Figure 21

The local modes represent the remains of the three separate modes of the three original groups, and when you see a bimodal or multimodal distribution your first suspicion is that it might have been produced by combining information from more than one group, each with different characteristics.

Combining two different groups into the same distribution doesn't always produce a bimodal distribution. *Figure 22* shows frequency distributions of the weights of adult men in the UK and adult women in the USA. Although we know that there are differences in the means for the two populations, that difference doesn't show up when they're combined. The difference in the means is quite small, and the spread of each distribution is quite large, so the separate peaks disappear when the two distributions are merged. Notice that the *spread* of the distribution has increased. I'll discuss what this means in the next session.

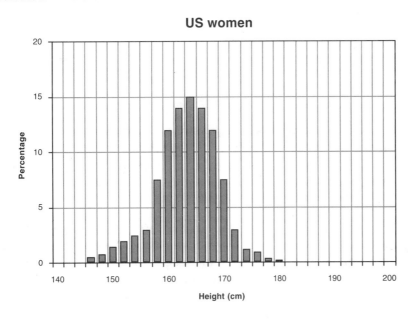

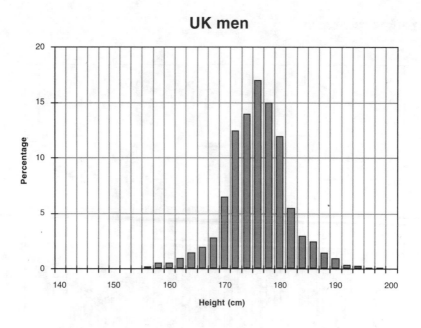

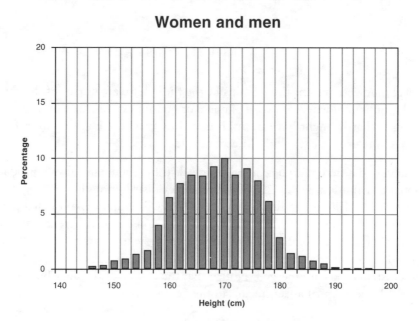

Figure 22

(I cheated slightly by choosing UK males and USA females. The difference between UK males and UK females is greater, and the two distributions don't combine to give such a smooth curve.)

Finding a multimodal distribution is no *proof* that separate groups contributed to the original data, just as only finding one distinct peak in a distribution doesn't necessarily mean that only one group is being represented. As I've mentioned before, looking at statistics this way can't provide proof of anything, but it can give a guide for speculation and further research.

So far, I've discussed using distributions in this 'preliminary diagnostic' way. You can look at a distribution, note irregularities and distortions from the ideal mathematical patterns and think 'That's unusual, I wonder if...?' and be guided into further investigation. This can be a powerful way of looking at data, but knowledge of the distribution of a set of measures about people can have another use. A frequency distribution summarises a whole set of measures in one graphic.

This enables us to compare any one observation with the overall pattern. We can judge whether that value is usual or unusual, and maybe estimate just how 'unusual' it is. This is the subject of the next session.

Summary

1. Large numbers of observations of a chance process tend to fall into a bell-shaped distribution.

2. Variations from the bell-shaped pattern may be used as a clue to the operation of non-random factors.

3. A common distortion of the symmetrical pattern is skewedness, where the peak of the distribution is pushed towards one end of the range. In skewed distributions, the mean, median and mode are likely to be different from each other.

4. Distributions with two or more humps (bimodal and multimodal distributions) are often produced by combining data from dissimilar groups.

Before you move on to Session Six, check that you have achieved the objectives given at the beginning of this session, and, if not, review the appropriate sections.

SESSION SIX

Measures of dispersion

Introduction

The last session offered reasons for the occurrence of frequency distributions of different shapes. One aspect of shape we haven't discussed yet is the amount of *spread* in the distribution. This measure gives an indication of how similar or different the individual measurements are from each other. Just as Session Four summarised the measures of central tendency in a set of numbers, so this session will introduce ways of summarising this spread in numbers.

Session objectives

At the end of this session you should be able to:

- understand that different sets of data have different degrees of internal variability

- define the terms quartile, decile and percentile

- understand the way in which the standard deviation may be used to represent the variability in a set of figures

- determine how common or rare a given value is compared to the overall sample from which it comes by using the standard deviation.

Understanding variability

ALLOW 10 MINUTES

Differences in dispersion

Figure 23 shows two frequency distributions. The means, medians and modes of the two sets of figures are the same. Write down two differences between them.

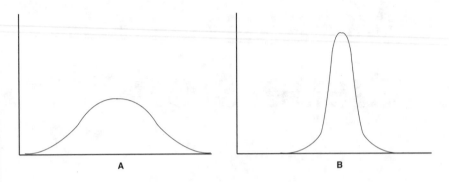

Figure 23

Dispersion *is the extent to which the values in a set of observations are different from each other. If all the values are similar, the dispersion is low. If there is a wide range of different values the dispersion is high. Standard deviation and interquartile range are measures of dispersion.*

Commentary:

Distribution A appears much more spread out than distribution B. This describes two related differences in the figures:

- the range for distribution A is greater than that for B

- in distribution A, there are more cases where an individual value is quite different from the mean; In B, nearly all the values are very similar.

The term **dispersion** describes this degree of spread in a distribution. Distribution A has a greater dispersion than distribution B.

ALLOW 10 MINUTES

How do height and weight differ?

Refer back to *Figures 2* (page 26) and *8* (page 39). Compare these graphs in terms of their dispersion. How easy is it to identify a difference?

Commentary:

There is a difference in dispersion between the two sets of figures, but it may not be immediately apparent from looking at the frequency distributions. Look at the two distributions below.

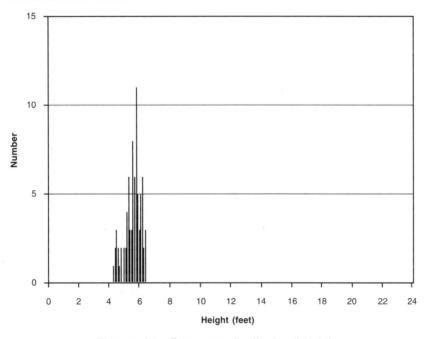

Figures 24a Frequency distribution (height)

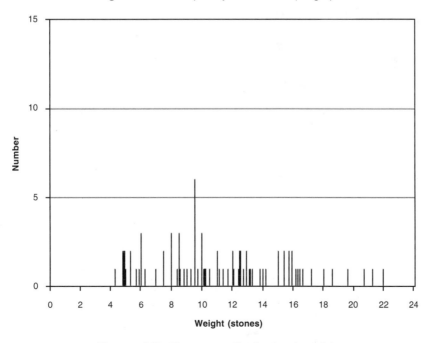

Figures 24b Frequency distribution (weight)

I hope it's clear from these that the weight values are much more spread out than the height values. The original presentations of the height and weight frequency distributions didn't make this difference so clear because they didn't use zero as the starting point of the horizontal scale. This is an example of how details of the presentation of a set of figures can make a big difference to the impression made. This is the subject of Session Eight.

Quartiles, deciles and percentiles

*A **measure of dispersion** is a measure which helps to describe the amount of dispersion, or variability, in a set of observations. The standard deviation and the interquartile range are common measures of dispersion.*

It's often important to know if a particular measurement is extreme or unusual compared with others. Consideration of the dispersion of a distribution can help in doing this. It's clear from the distributions above that a height of 7 feet is very unusual in this sample, but a weight of 15 stones, although quite different from the sample mean (11.2 stones) is not too unusual. Expression of the degree of difference or unusualness of a value can be made more precise by using one of a set of statistics called **measures of dispersion**.

Quartiles

*A **quartile** is the measure that divides a ranked set of observations into groups that each contain 25%, or a quarter, of the observations. The first quartile is the value that divides the bottom 25% of the observations from the rest. The 3rd quartile divides the bottom 75% from the top 25%.*

The most straightforward approach to describing dispersion numerically comes from dividing the observations into equal-sized groups. The median is a way of doing this. It divides a set of numbers into halves, one with values greater than the median, the other with values less than the median. This approach can be extended by dividing the set of values into four, to give **quartiles**. The first quartile is that value exceeded by three quarters of the group, the second quartile is the value exceeded by half the group (so the second quartile is exactly the same as the median) and the third quartile is the value exceeded by one quarter of the group. The greater the dispersion of the original measurements, the greater the differences between the quartiles.

So if a value falls below the first quartile, you can tell that it is unusual to the extent that it's in the bottom 25% of the overall set of values. This seems a useful start, but it's a fairly crude measure.

Deciles and percentiles

ACTIVITY 29   ALLOW **10** MINUTES

A more precise measure than the quartile

Propose one way of extending this approach to provide a more sensitive measure of dispersion than the quartile.

Commentary:

A reasonable approach is to find the values which define smaller and smaller groups in the distribution. Instead of dividing into four sub-groups, you could divide into eight, or 16.... This is the route that statisticians have followed, but they haven't quite followed on from quartiles. The other commonly-used divisions are deciles, which divide a set of numbers into ten equal parts, and percentiles, which define one hundred equal parts of a distribution. Percentiles are often used to help evaluate information about the health care of children, so we'll use that as the basis for the next activity.

A **decile** *is the measure that divides a ranked set of observations into groups that each contain 10%, or one tenth, of the observations. The first decile is the value that divides the bottom 10% of the observations from the rest. The 7th decile divides the bottom 70% from the top 30%.*

ACTIVITY 30

ALLOW **10** MINUTES

Percentiles in health care

Four six-year-old girls are weighed as part of a school health check. Their weights are:

Amy, 21 kg; Rowena, 19.5 kg; Debbie, 17 kg; Dawn, 14 kg

Table 6 shows percentile weights for British girls aged five years and six months.

Percentile	3	10	30	50	70	90	97
Wt. (kg)	16	17	19	20.5	22	24	27

Table 6

Some of these children weigh less than the median (50th percentile) weight for their age. Compare the data from the school health check with that in the table, noting any unusual values. Would any of the girls' weights give you cause for concern?

Commentary:

If you identified any value as 'unusual' then you made a value judgement: greater understanding of statistics can help to clarify what the numbers *tell you*, but it takes clinical knowledge and experience to know what that *means*.

A further point is that the raw figures of weight need interpreting in terms of children's basic body build, their lifestyle, and anything known about their medical history. A single statistic is no substitute for wider knowledge of an individual. A marked *change* over time in the percentile that a child's weight corresponds with might be more likely to raise concern than any particular value.

All the same, the information in the activity gives you the basis for a start of an answer.

Amy's weight, at 21 kg, is very close to the 50th percentile. This is also the median weight. From the definition of the median it follows that half the population are lighter, half heavier: from the definition of a percentile it follows that 50% of the population are heavier than the 50th percentile, and 50% are lighter. 50% and one half are the same, so the two measures coincide. On the assumption that the distribution of children's weights is like that of the bell-shaped distributions that were discussed in the last session, a weight near to the median will be pretty common. Amy's weight is not unusual.

Rowena's weight falls just above the 30th percentile: 30% of the population of children her age are lighter than her, 70% heavier. So roughly two out of three of those children are heavier than her. That still doesn't seem unusual to me.

Debbie, at 17 kg, falls on the tenth percentile. She's lighter than 90% of children her age. Perhaps that's quite unusual, but not worrying.

Dawn is 14 kg and her weight is less than the third percentile (see *Figure 25*). Only three children in a hundred are lighter than the third percentile weight. Perhaps her weight should give cause for concern: we should find out more.

You may know that standard charts showing percentile weights for growing children are produced, and one is reproduced in *Figure 25*. The information could be shown as a series of tables, one for each age, but it's more compact and convenient to express the information in graphical form.

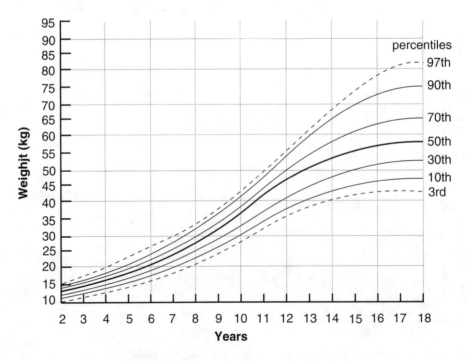

Figure 25 Girl's weight 2–18 years

ACTIVITY 31　　　　　ALLOW **10** MINUTES

Expressing percentiles in tables or as graphs

I derived the small table of information I gave you in the last activity from the data in *Figure 25*. That table is repeated below, with an extra line for the corresponding values for seven-year-olds. Complete the table using data from *Figure 25*.

Percentile	3	10	30	50	70	90	97
Wt. (kg) for 6-year-old girls	16	17	19	20.5	22	24	27
Wt. (kg) for 7-year-old girls							

Table 7

Commentary:

The completed table is:

Percentile	3	10	30	50	70	90	97
Wt. (kg) for 6-year-old girls	16	17	19	20.5	22	24	27
Wt. (kg) for 7-year-old girls	17	18.5	21	23	25	27	30.5

Table 8

It is difficult to read numerical values precisely from a chart like this, so your values may differ slightly from mine (but 1 kg either way is near enough). This isn't just sloppiness: although it might be possible to measure people's weights very accurately, and specify percentile levels with great precision, that accuracy may not be appropriate. Even if we trust our scales, they are not measuring a fixed quantity: a good meal or a visit to the toilet could easily change someone's weight by half a kilogram in the short term. In that case, specifying values to a similar degree of precision seems appropriate, not sloppy.

Quartiles as a way of expressing range

In Session Four, *Activity 16*, I suggested that the midpoint of the range is not very useful as a descriptive statistic because it's only influenced by the two values which lie at the extremes. A statistic based on the difference between the first and third quartiles, the range that covers the cases between 25% and 75% of the way up the rankings, isn't influenced by the extremes, but serves a similar purpose to the midpoint of the range. This statistic is called the **interquartile range** (or sometimes the **semi-interquartile range**) and it is useful measure of the 'middle half' of a distribution, especially one that is based on rank data.

*The **interquartile range** is the difference between the first and third quartiles. A measure which defines the 50% of the observed values which are closest to the median. The interquartile range is a measure of dispersion. It is sometimes referred to as the semi-interquartile range.*

The standard deviation

*The **standard deviation** is a measure of dispersion. The greater the standard deviation, the greater the range of values observed. In the normal distribution, 68% of the observed values fall between one standard deviation above the mean and one standard deviation below the mean. The interquartile range is another measure of dispersion.*

Quartiles, deciles and percentiles give an indication of how a distribution is spread out in terms of the different proportions of the observations which fall below certain values. There is, however, a more direct measure of spread than this, one that has a high value for a distribution with a wide spread, and a small value for a distribution with a narrow spread. This measure of deviation describes the amount of difference between the individual measures and the mean of the whole set of figures, and is called the **standard deviation** (SD).

It is a kind of 'average difference from the mean' for the whole distribution. Most introductory statistics books discuss how the standard deviation is derived, and Derek Rowntree's *Statistics Without Tears* has a straightforward account.

What I would like to make clear in this unit is how the standard deviation varies as the shape of the distribution changes, and how the standard deviation can be used to give information about how unusual individual values are. I'll start with the relationship between the standard deviation and the shape of the distribution.

Refer back to *Figure 23* (page 64). Both distributions have the same mean, mode and median, but the values of their standard deviation are different. Can you identify the one with the larger standard deviation?

Clearly distribution A is more spread out, so it has the larger standard deviation.

*The **normal distribution** is a particular mathematically produced frequency distribution. It is similar to those real-life distributions produced by summarising large numbers of random events. The normal distribution is symmetrical. The mean, median and mode are all at the same value. The relationship between the standard deviation and the proportion of observations in any part of the distribution is precisely defined. These well-defined features of the normal distribution are often useful in helping to analyse sets of real-life data which approximate to it (they are said to approximate to normality). Normal and normality in this sense have nothing to do with normal in the everyday sense.*

In Session Five, we talked about 'perfect chance distributions' and suggested that they are regular and symmetrical, while distributions of real observations are often less regular. One perfect distribution that statisticians use is called the normal distribution. The 'normal' in the name *doesn't* mean 'usual' – the word comes from the mathematical idea of 'norm'. Fortunately for the statisticians it does approximate closely to many large sets of real-world observations. The reason for introducing it here is because the standard deviation has a close relationship with the **normal distribution**. For a start, the range of a normal distribution is roughly equal to 6 standard deviations.

ACTIVITY 32   ALLOW **10** MINUTES

Estimating standard deviation from range

One of the distributions below has a standard deviation of 5, the other has a standard deviation of 10. Which is which?.

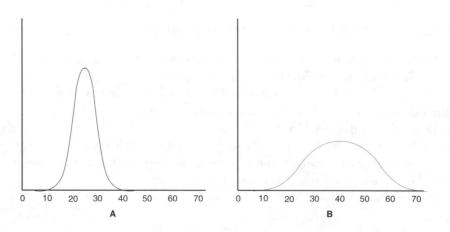

Figure 26

Commentary:

The range for graph A is 30, so the standard deviation is roughly 30/6, or 5.

For B, with a wider range of 60, the standard deviation is about 10 (60/10).

The standard deviation is useful as a way of summing up the spread of a distribution (it plays the same part among measures of dispersion as the mean does among measures of central tendency), but it also turns out that it can be used to divide the distribution up into quite meaningful chunks.

ACTIVITY 33

ALLOW **10** MINUTES

Standard deviation and proportions of a distribution

Here's another distribution (*Figure 27*). This time I've drawn in lines which show the values which lie within 1, 2 and 3 SDs on either side of the mean.

Describe in words the proportion of the shaded area as a proportion of the total area of the curves in *Figure 27* when the area is:

● 1 SD either side of the mean
● 2 SDs either side of the mean
● 3 SDs either side of the mean.

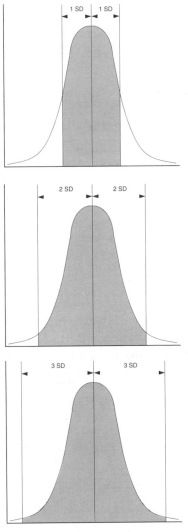

Figure 27

Commentary:

You can't make an absolutely accurate estimate from such basic figures, but the following seem reasonable estimates.

- More than half the area lies within 1 SD either way from the mean.

- The great majority of the area falls within 2 SDs either way.

- Hardly any of the area falls outside 3 SDs either way.

The mathematically precise answers are as follows.

- 68.0% of the observations fall within 1 SD either side of the mean. This means that about one third of the observations fall between the mean and 1 SD above the mean, and one third fall between the mean and 1 SD below, since the distribution is symmetrical.

- 95.0% (19 out of 20) of the observations fall within 2 SDs either side of the mean.

- 99.7% (almost all) of the observations fall within 3 SDs either side of the mean.

These values are really a mathematical accident, but it's a very fortunate accident. It means that there's a convenient measure which chops the distribution up into the middle two-thirds, the great majority, and all but the most extreme variations.

This is only true for the mathematically ideal normal distribution, of course, but many measurements on large numbers of people *do* give distributions very close to a normal distribution.

This may also seem a little vague and abstract, so the next activity should put these ideas into a practical context.

ACTIVITY 34

Standard deviations and blood pressure

Suppose that from measurements of very many people it is found that the mean diastolic blood pressure of 35-year-old British males is 80 mm/Hg, with a standard deviation of 11 mm/Hg.

From these figures what range of values of diastolic blood pressure would you expect to find in a random group of 35-year-olds?

If one person had a diastolic pressure of 120 mm/Hg would this be unusual or not?

Commentary

I've said that two thirds of the population fall within 1 SD on either side of the mean, so values between 69 and 91 mm/Hg should be quite common. Amongst 200 individuals you might find some values as extreme as 58 or 102 mm/Hg.

A value of 120 mm/Hg is more than 3 SDs away from the mean, so must be very unusual.

Of course, you could have made the same sort of judgements with a table or chart of percentiles, but the power of the standard deviation is that only two figures, the mean and the standard deviation, are required to describe the whole distribution.

Limitations of the standard deviation

Quick estimates of the size of different parts of a population only work like this when the distribution is symmetrical, not skewed, and is very like the normal distribution. In other cases, it's always possible to calculate the standard deviation, and it still gives an estimate of the degree of spread of the distribution, but the convenient relationship between the standard deviation and the proportions of the distribution no longer holds. Just as the mean can be biased by unusually high or low values, so the standard deviation can be artificially inflated by an extreme value.

For irregular distributions it is better to use percentiles rather than the standard deviation.

ACTIVITY 35 ALLOW 10 MINUTES

Measures of dispersion and different kinds of measure

The standard deviation, like the mean, uses calculations which depend on the numerical values of all the observations, so it's only right to use the standard deviation with quantity measures.

But what if the original observations were rankings? Identify another measure of dispersion that would be better than the standard deviation.

Commentary:

Quartiles and percentiles are based on ranking, (the lowest quarter, the highest 5%, and so on) so they are appropriate measures of dispersion for ranked data. They are related to the median, the measure of central tendency that's based on ranking. For normal distributions, the median corresponds to the mean, the measure of central tendency often used with quantity measures. Similarly, the interquartile range, which defines the middle half of a ranked distribution, corresponds with the range of two standard deviations, which defines the middle two-thirds of a distribution based on quantity measures.

It's not reasonable to construct a distribution from category observations, because each category is separate from the others, and shouldn't be combined, so there's no category measure of dispersion that is related to the mode.

Ways of describing scattergrams

This session has been all about ways of describing distributions and their shape numerically. It's possible to do the same kind of thing with one of the other kinds of presentation I talked about in Session Three – the scattergram. Correlation coefficients are concerned with the problem of describing the shape and patterns of scattergrams, and that is the subject of the next session.

Summary

1. Distributions can differ in the extent to which they are spread out – their dispersion.

2. Dispersion can be described by dividing the distribution into portions – quartiles, deciles and percentiles.

2. The standard deviation (SD) is a convenient and powerful way of describing the dispersion of distributions that approximate to the normal distribution, particularly if the observations are quantity measures.

Before you move on to Session Seven, check that you have achieved the objectives given at the beginning of this session, and, if not, review the appropriate sections.

Correlation

Introduction

Scattergrams were introduced in Session Three as a way of getting an overall picture of how two sets of measures (like height and weight) were related to each other. This session will concentrate on the way they can be used to identify trends in the data and then introduce another statistic, the correlation coefficient, as a measure of those trends.

The first activity provides further practice in interpreting scattergrams.

Session objectives

At the end of this session you should be able to:

- use scattergrams to detect trends and patterns in sets of data

- describe the use of the correlation coefficient as a measure of the agreement between two sets of measures

- state the meaning of positive and negative correlation, and be able to roughly interpret numerical values of the correlation coefficient

- understand that some aspects of the relationships between sets of observations are not well represented by the correlation coefficient

- appreciate that correlation coefficients do not imply any causal relationship between factors.

Trends and patterns

Interpreting scattergrams

Below are four scattergrams showing the sets of observations on various measures (the axes are labelled). They are height and weight, age and blood pressure, hair length and income, and age of car and its value.

Describe in words the relationship between the variables shown for each scattergram.

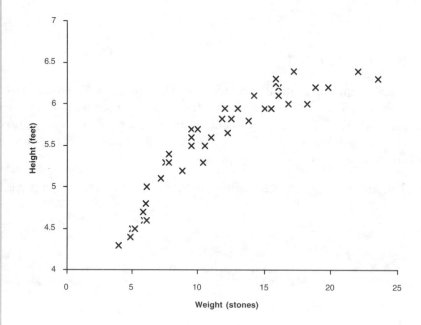

Figure 28a

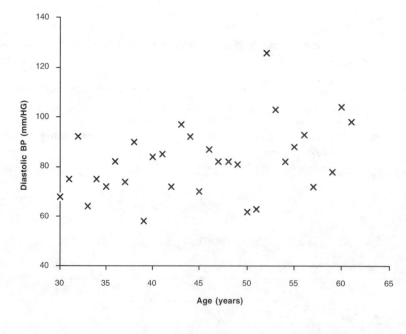

Figure 28b

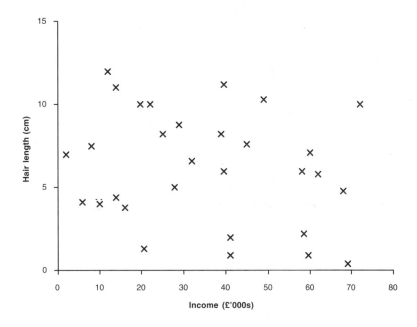

Figure 28c

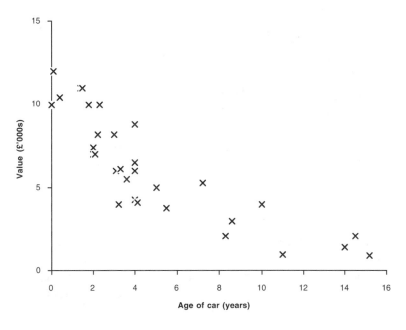

Figure 28d

Commentary:

a) The scattergram of height and weight shows a strong tendency for height and weight to increase together. This relationship levels off a little at the higher weights, and can be called non-linear. I will discuss **non-linear** patterns later in this session.

b) Blood pressure and age also tend to increase together, but the relationship is not so definite and clear as in graph (a). There are more cases that don't fit with the main trend.

c) It's difficult to see any relationship here because the points seem to be spread randomly all over the scattergram.

d) Value decreases as age increases. The pattern is a bit like graph (a), but in reverse.

Scattergrams can help to identify trends, especially if they are as marked as in *Figure 28a* or *28d*. However, a numerical measure that expresses the trend is easier to present, gives a more precise estimate of the strength of the trend and provides a value which can be used in inferential statistics.

The correlation coefficient

The correlation coefficient *is a statistic used to express the similarity between two sets of observations. If measures on one variable tend to increase as measures on the other variable increase, the value of the correlation coefficient will be positive. If one set of values tends to decrease as the other increases, then the correlation will be negative. If there is no consistent pattern in the relationship between the two sets of measures, the correlation will be near zero. The value of the correlation coefficient can only vary over a range between +1 and -1.*

This numerical measure is called the **correlation coefficient**. The term 'correlation' gives a hint to the meaning of the value, which is to do with the co-relatedness of sets of measures – whether they go together or not. You will find that the terms 'correlation' and 'correlation coefficient' are both commonly used.

Because of the way they're worked out, the only possible values that correlation coefficients can have are between +1 and -1. A correlation of +1 means a perfect positive relationship: as the values of one variable increase, so do the values of the other, and there are no exceptions to this rule. A zero value suggests no relationship between the two sets of variables. If the correlation coefficient is negative, it shows that measures of one variable decrease as measures of the other variable increase. A coefficient of -1 reflects a perfect negative relationship.

The more consistent the pattern of the relationship, the further the value of the correlation coefficient is from zero, and the nearer it is to +1 or -1, depending on the direction of the relationship.

ACTIVITY 37   ALLOW **10** MINUTES

Values of correlation coefficients

Below are the same scattergrams as in the previous exercise, together with a new one (for volume and weight of jam).

Make an estimate of the value of the correlation coefficient which describes each set of data. Is it likely to be positive, negative or near zero? Will it be large (nearer +1 or -1) or small (nearer zero)?

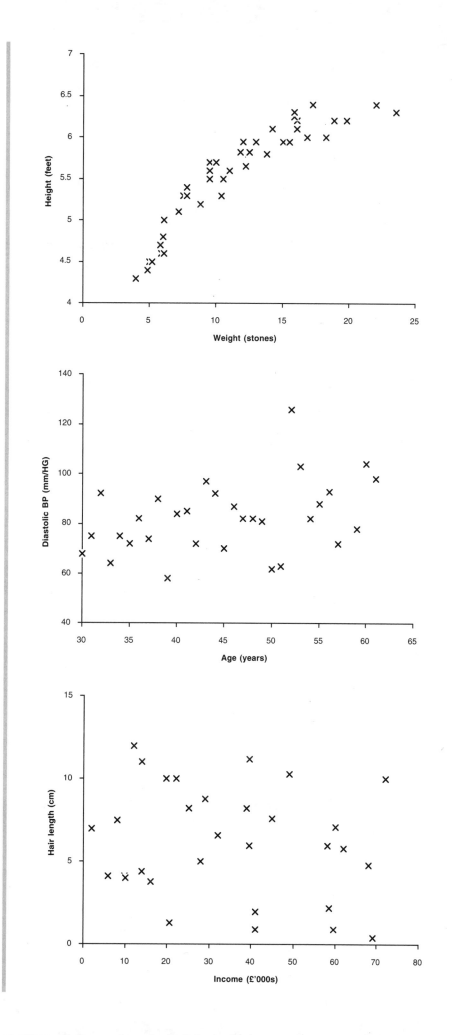

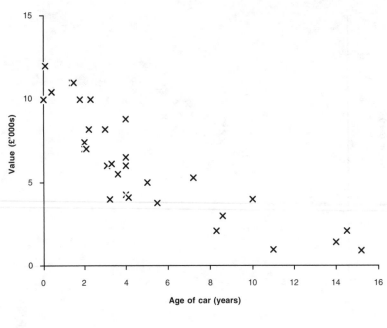

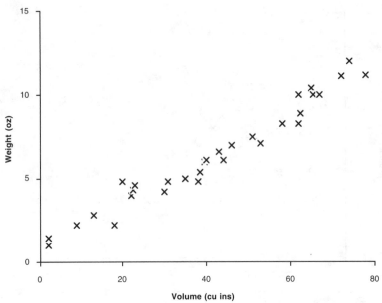

Figure 29

Commentary:

a) The correlation is positive and close to 1. The measures of both variables increase together.

b) The correlation is positive but the value will not be as high as for a). The trend is in the same direction, but is not so marked.

c) I would expect the correlation coefficient here to be close to zero. It's difficult to estimate just how random a set of observations are by eye, but there is certainly no obvious pattern here.

d) A fairly strong negative correlation: one value goes down as the other increases. The pattern is fairly consistent, but not as clear as in a). The value of the coefficient should be further from zero than in b), but not so far from zero as that for scattergram a).

e) The relationship here is almost perfectly consistent (put a ruler along the points and you'll find they make a good straight line). The two variables increase in step with one another.

I worked out the values for each of the sets of data.

a) Height and weight: +0.8

b) Blood pressure and age: +0.4

c) Hair length and income: -0.15

d) Car value and age: -0.9

e) Weight and volume: The correlation will be close to +1

In the case of c), hair length and income, you might be surprised that such an apparently random pattern still gave a value which was some way from zero. In fact, because of the way the calculation comes out, quite big differences in the value of the coefficient near to zero don't correspond to big differences in the consistency of the pattern. The difference between a correlation coefficient of 0.1 and 0.15 is negligible, whereas the difference between 0.9 and 0.95 is very marked. So the value -0.15 is effectively very near zero. The difference between the strength of the pattern suggested by the values of 0.8 for height and weight, and -0.9 for car age and value, is quite large.

From previous sessions you'll know that there are parallel sets of statistics, one for rank variables and one for quantity variables. In this session the rank order method has been used to calculate the correlation coefficient for you. This is partly for consistency and partly because that method is reasonable for most sets of measures. Quantity variables work well as rank variables, while rank variables may not be adequate as quantity variables.

Category variables can't be organised on to a sensible scale, so you can't use them to produce scattergrams or to calculate correlation coefficients.

Interpreting correlation coefficients

ACTIVITY 38 ALLOW **10** MINUTES

What do particular values of the correlation coefficient tell us?

Here are three problems. Choose what you think is the best answer for each one and note it down before going on to the commentary.

a) A study found a positive correlation between age and wealth. Does this mean that:

1) older people tend to be poorer than younger people

2) younger people tend to be poorer than older people

3) getting old makes you richer

4) riches cause you to age more rapidly

5) getting old makes you poorer?

b) Which of the following terms best describes the correlation between age and likelihood of dying in the next 20 years for adults:

1) negative

2) positive

3) zero

4) negative or positive

5) there's no way of telling?

c) The correlation between the bank balances of students financed by termly grants and the number of days left in the term is:

1) positive

2) negative

3) around zero

4) it's impossible to say?

Commentary:

a) Age and wealth

The second answer is best. The positive correlation shows a tendency for people who are older also to be more wealthy. 2) and 3) are right about the direction of the change, but these answers suggest something about what caused that change. Correlations in themselves don't tell anything about cause. I'll come back to this point later in the session.

b) Age and likelihood of dying

Answer 2) seems sensible: as your age increases, your chances of further long survival decrease. (Sorry about that.)

A correlation around zero (answer 3) suggests there's no clear relationship between the two measures. In this case, I would expect a pattern – you can't live forever.

Answer 5) is probably right for any one individual. But for a large group, a clear trend should emerge. Insurance companies know this: they charge a lot more for 20-year life cover at 60 than at 20.

c) Finance and term time.

Answer 1), positive, is right. Correlations will be positive if both measures tend to change in the same direction. In this case, they both go down at the same time – but they do both change in the same direction.

Answer 2) seems reasonable on the surface, but it's wrong. Although both are going down at the same time, which seems negative (running out of money and time to study at the same time), they're both changing in the same direction.

Answer 3) would suggest that bank balances stayed about the same or varied randomly as the term went on. This might be right for students who are not financed by a termly payment like a grant cheque.

Relationships which are not detected by correlation coefficients

Not all relationships between two sets of data show up well in the correlation coefficient. The next two activities illustrate two ways in which this might happen.

ACTIVITY 39   ALLOW **10** MINUTES

Reducing the range

Figure 30 a shows the familiar scattergram of weight and height from Session Three, and a version of the same figure (*30b*) that only shows those people between 5.6 feet and 5.9 feet. The correlation for all the values shown in the *Figure 30a* scattergram is +0.88. Estimate the value of the correlation coefficient for those values shown in *Figure 30b*.

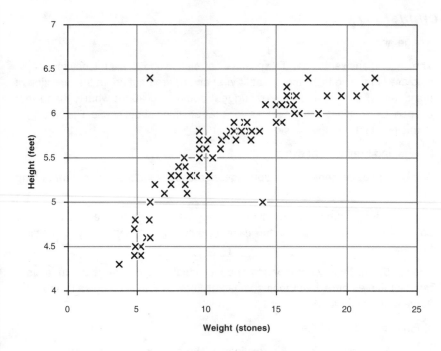

Figure 30a Scattergram of height and weight

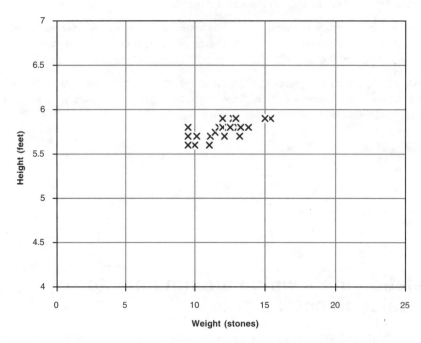

Figure 30b Scattergram of height and weight

Commentary:

It's very difficult to estimate low correlations by eye, but a reasonable guess is that the value would be much lower than for the full range. In fact, it works out at about +0.4.

When you consider the whole group, which covers a wide range of heights and weights, the pattern is clear and shows up strongly in the correlation coefficient. When you focus in on a restricted range of values, the overall pattern no longer appears, and this is reflected in the correlation coefficient. This isn't a fault of correlation as a measure, but a reflection of the dangers of using a restricted range of measures to describe a trend. It does reflect a common frustration in research. A pattern may show up in a preliminary, crude, wide-ranging survey but a much more careful study of just that group which is most affected or most relevant shows no pattern at all. This is the statistical version of not being able to see the forest for the trees.

ACTIVITY 40   ALLOW **10** MINUTES

Non-linear patterns

The graphs, *Figures 31a* to *c*, show three patterns of relationship between observations on two variables. The correlation coefficients for the three cases are about +0.8, +0.4 and +0.2. Which value goes with which figure?

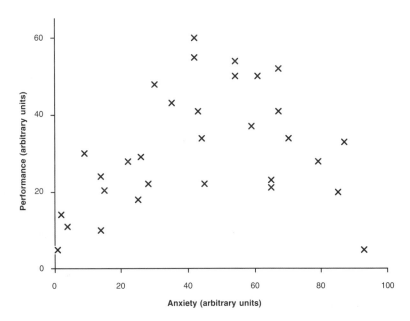

Figure 31a

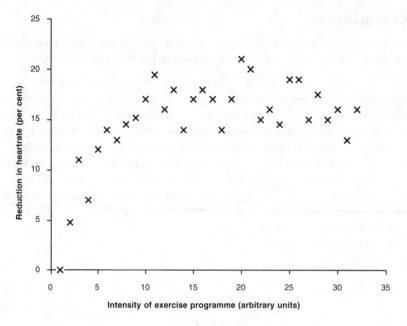

Figure 31b

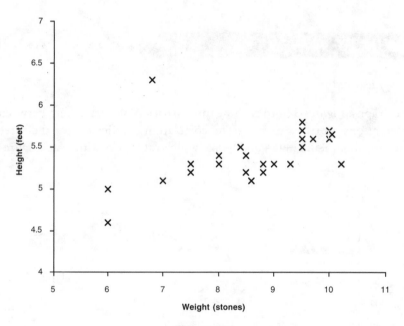

Figure 31c

Commentary:

It's possible to draw curves through these graphs, showing that there seems to be a strong relationship between the measures in each case. However the only graph that comes close to having a straight line in it is c), with a high correlation coefficient of +0.8. Graph a), where the direction of the relationship changes midway, gives a low correlation of +0.2. Graph b) is in between with +0.4.

When the relationship doesn't follow a straight line the size of the correlation coefficient is reduced. In a) it's almost as though the two halves of the graph cancel each other out to give a final result approaching zero.

The **non-linear relationships** in a) and b) are not well detected by correlation coefficients. In real life, patterns like this are very common: the effects of different levels of drug dosage, the enjoyment produced by spending different amounts of time on a certain activity, the increase in quality gained by spending more on a product, for example. All of these effects may start off by increasing, then level off or go into decline at higher levels. It's the well-known law of diminishing returns. In cases like this, it's better to look at all the data, perhaps in a scattergram, rather than rely on a correlation coefficient to sum it up effectively.

When the relationship is non-linear, using different ways of calculating the correlation coefficient will give different results. Methods based on the rank-order are less affected by non-linearity than methods which use the actual values observed. This is because there may still be a consistent order in the *ranks*, even when the differences between *values* are quite varied.

A non-linear relationship is one in which there is not a simple consistent pattern of relationship between two variables. A common non-linear pattern is one in which values of one variable increase as the other increases, up to a certain point, but then one set of values levels of or falls with further increase of the other. The relationship between dosage and sense of well-being for some recreational drugs like alcohol follows a non-linear pattern.

Correlation and causation

All through this unit I've said that descriptive statistics prove nothing, and the assessment of causality and proof is a matter for research and inferential statistics. The same applies to correlation: a high correlation between the number of cigarettes people smoke and their chances of dying of lung cancer does *not* prove that smoking causes cancer. Correlation coefficients can't be used to establish the cause of an observation because they are only measures of agreement between sets of figures: at best they can only establish a consistent pattern, not explain why that pattern appears. Of course, correlational results may prompt a *suspicion* about causation which can then be tested out by experimental or epidemiological study. The next two activities will reinforce this point.

ACTIVITY 41	ALLOW 15 MINUTES

Correlation and causation

A strong positive correlation exists between household income and household distance from the city centre, for an area within a five mile radius of the centre. Explain why a move from the inner city to the suburbs would not make me better off.

Commentary:

Although the result suggests that households in the suburbs have higher incomes, it doesn't show that it's the distance that causes the income. Correlation doesn't tell you anything about cause. It's much more likely that households with higher income are found further out because richer families can afford more expensive housing in the leafy suburbs, have more access to transport and so on.

ACTIVITY 42 ALLOW 10 MINUTES

Which causes which?

Several studies in Europe and America have shown positive correlations between any two of these three:

- years spent in education

- measured intelligence

- status of adult occupation.

Suggest some possible explanations for these relationships. Might other factors be lurking in the background?

Commentary:

A multitude of explanations exists for these relationships. Perhaps high intelligence causes people to spend a long time in education and allows them to gain high status employment. Or maybe spending a long time in school increases your IQ score. Two other factors not mentioned which might have an influence are parental occupation and parental intelligence. Perhaps one or both of them is the causative factor behind the three measures mentioned in the problem. The argument may be as much to do with political beliefs as with social science evidence. In any case, the correlations don't give any answer about causation. They merely show what patterns have been observed.

Correlation as a useful research technique

Although correlation is not a powerful technique for showing up non-linear relationships between variables, and it cannot be used to establish the cause of any effect, it is a very valuable technique. In many studies in subjects like nutrition and epidemiology it isn't possible to do the kind of carefully controlled trials that allow simple experimental/control or before/after comparisons. The best that can be done is to gather lots of information from the general population and then sift through it, looking for patterns. Calculating correlations between sets of measures is a good way of doing this, especially where the effects are small and variable, but consistent enough to show up mathematically with very large numbers of observations.

Another approach is to try to use graphical techniques to show up patterns. The scattergram is one approach, but there are examples in the next session of other ways of doing this. I'll also discuss how graphical presentation may be used to distort the information given by the original data.

Summary

1. Trends and patterns in scattergrams can be expressed mathematically by the correlation coefficient, which has values in the range +1 to -1.

2. A value of +1 for the correlation between two variables shows a direct positive relationship between them; a value of -1 shows a direct negative relationship between them; and a value of around zero for the correlation coefficient suggests no consistent relationship between the two variables.

3. Correlation coefficients are not very sensitive at detecting non-linear relationships between variables.

4. Correlation is a useful technique for detecting patterns, but it gives no evidence about causation, which requires other methods of investigation.

Before you move on to Session Eight check that you have achieved the objectives given at the beginning of this session, and, if not, review the appropriate sections.

SESSION EIGHT

Graphical presentation

Introduction

I have introduced several forms of graphical presentation in earlier sessions. This session will examine the purposes, techniques and dangers of graphical presentation more thoroughly, and introduce you to some new graphical techniques which have not been mentioned so far.

Session objectives

At the end of this session you should be able to:

- give reasons for the graphical presentation of statistical data

- select appropriate graphical presentations for various statistical purposes

- describe several techniques which can be used to distort the impressions given in graphical presentations

- identify inappropriate ways of presenting information graphically.

Terminology

There is a small problem of terminology here. Common ways of referring to 'graphical presentations of statistics' are to use the words 'figure' (which might be confused with 'figure' meaning 'number') or 'graph' (which suggests a particular kind of presentation which isn't appropriate to all the techniques discussed in this chapter). Because of these ambiguities, I will avoid these words and instead refer to visual presentations of statistical information as 'graphics'. The word may seem ugly, but it's short, and I hope it will be clear in this context.

Why present data graphically?

The first question is, 'Why use graphics instead of numerical statistics?' Let's try to identify some general reasons for their use.

ACTIVITY 43 ALLOW **15** MINUTES

What's the point of graphics?

Figures 32a to *g* show a selection of statistical graphics. The editors of the publications represented had good reasons for presenting information in this way rather than in numbers. Note down as many of these reasons as you can. You could also use the material you collected for *Activity 3*.

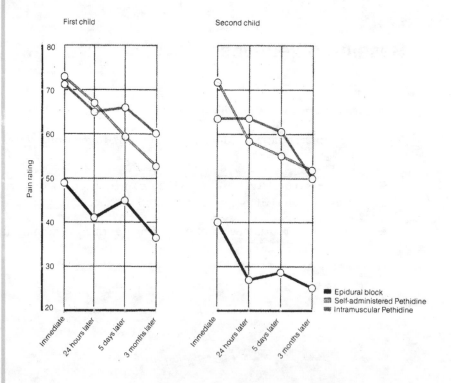

Figure 32a

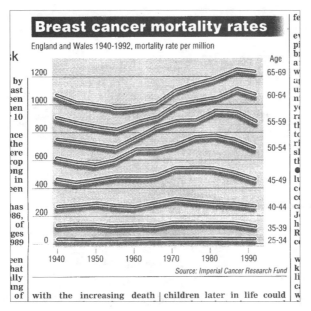

Figure 32b

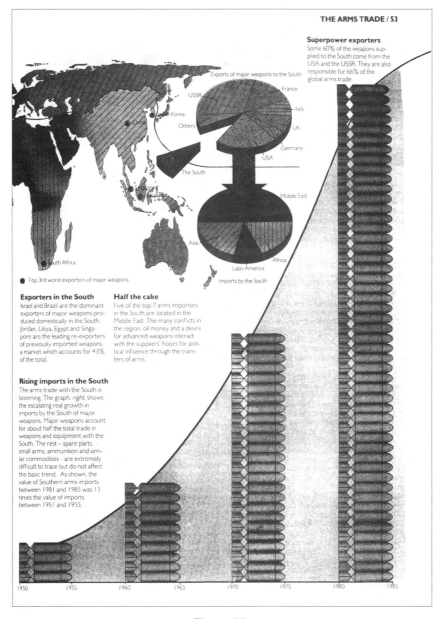

Figure 32c

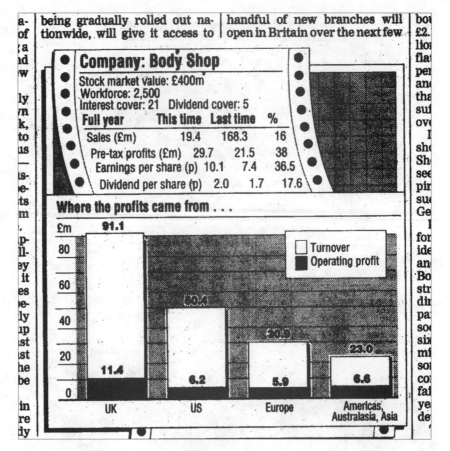

Figure 32d

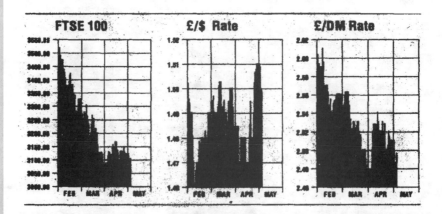

Figure 32e

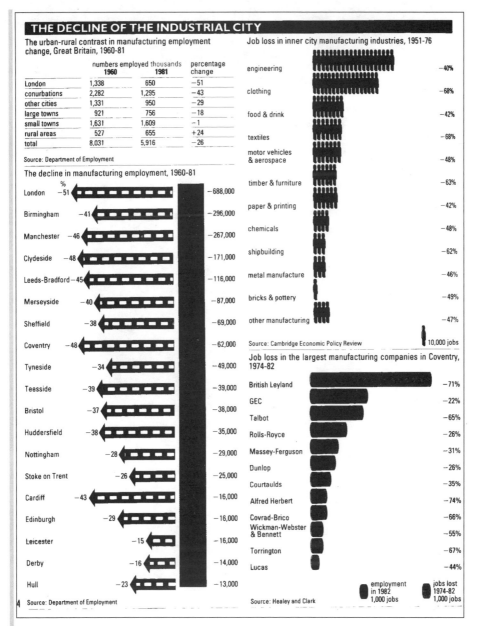

THE DECLINE OF THE INDUSTRIAL CITY

The urban-rural contrast in manufacturing employment change, Great Britain, 1960-81

| | numbers employed thousands | | percentage change |
	1960	1981	
London	1,338	650	−51
conurbations	2,282	1,295	−43
other cities	1,331	950	−29
large towns	921	756	−18
small towns	1,631	1,609	−1
rural areas	527	655	+24
total	8,031	5,916	−26

Source: Department of Employment

The decline in manufacturing employment, 1960-81

	%	
London	−51	−688,000
Birmingham	−41	−296,000
Manchester	−46	−267,000
Clydeside	−48	−171,000
Leeds-Bradford	−45	−116,000
Merseyside	−40	−87,000
Sheffield	−38	−69,000
Coventry	−48	−62,000
Tyneside	−34	−49,000
Teesside	−39	−39,000
Bristol	−37	−38,000
Huddersfield	−38	−35,000
Nottingham	−28	−29,000
Stoke on Trent	−26	−25,000
Cardiff	−43	−16,000
Edinburgh	−29	−16,000
Leicester	−15	−16,000
Derby	−16	−14,000
Hull	−23	−13,000

Source: Department of Employment

Job loss in inner city manufacturing industries, 1951-76

engineering	−40%
clothing	−68%
food & drink	−42%
textiles	−68%
motor vehicles & aerospace	−48%
timber & furniture	−63%
paper & printing	−42%
chemicals	−48%
shipbuilding	−62%
metal manufacture	−46%
bricks & pottery	−49%
other manufacturing	−47%

10,000 jobs

Source: Cambridge Economic Policy Review

Job loss in the largest manufacturing companies in Coventry, 1974-82

British Leyland	−71%
GEC	−22%
Talbot	−65%
Rolls-Royce	−26%
Massey-Ferguson	−31%
Dunlop	−26%
Courtaulds	−35%
Alfred Herbert	−74%
Covrad-Brico	−66%
Wickman-Webster & Bennett	−55%
Torrington	−67%
Lucas	−44%

employment in 1982 1,000 jobs
jobs lost 1974-82 1,000 jobs

Source: Healey and Clark

Figure 32f

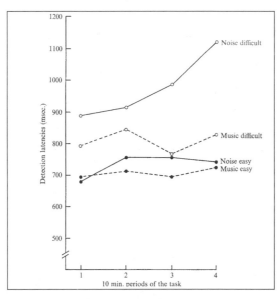

Figure 32g

Commentary:

There are a range of reasons. Some might not be to do with statistical presentation at all, such as brightening up a page of text. The main functional ones that occurred to me were:

● to bring together a large amount of data so that it can readily be shown in one presentation

● to simplify complex data, in the hope of seeing patterns or significant features in it

● to highlight trends and patterns

● to make a statistical point forcefully

● to make it easier for the readership to understand a point.

The use of graphics for the presentation of statistics supports two purposes: to *see* (i.e. to perceive) and to *show* (i.e. to summarise).

Seeing: When someone has gathered statistical information as a way of finding out about something, graphics may be a powerful way of helping them to *see* (perceive) the information hidden in the mass of numbers. I hope that some of the graphics showing information about height and weight used in the earlier sessions show how this can be done.

Showing: When researchers feel they have an understanding of the patterns behind the data, when they have a story to tell, graphics may be the quickest and most compelling way of getting the message over.

These different purposes may require different kinds of graphics, but they both give rise to similar questions.

● What is this graphic for? What is its function?

● Does it fulfil this purpose better than a numerical presentation or an alternative graphic?

Using graphics to explore the data

You have already explored one data set, that of height and weight. In some of the earlier activities you identified the way in which graphics can help in the understanding of numerical statistics. Now let's examine in some detail the way in which the graphical presentation of geographical information might be helpful in epidemiological work.

ACTIVITY 44 ALLOW **10** MINUTES

Interpreting geographical information

Figure 33 is a street map of nineteenth century London. The circles show the pumps from which the population got all their water and the small dots show cases of a fatal illness. Can you make any guesses about the source of illness? Is there any public health action you would recommend?

Figure 33

Commentary:

The cases seem clustered around the pump in Broad Street, so it seems reasonable to suppose that contracting the disease is connected with using water from this pump. Preventing use of this water might reduce cases of the disease.

The original of this map was produced by Dr John Snow on investigating an outbreak of cholera in 1854. The work helped to establish the link between cholera and contaminated water. Snow's public health action was simple and direct: he had the handle removed from the pump in Broad Street and this ended an epidemic in which more than 500 people had died.

Snow's map just shows yes/no information: a mark appears for every fatality. The next example is more complicated, with markings that show different levels of a variable.

A complex geographical presentation

The map below (*Figure 34a*) shows incidence of stomach cancer in white men in the USA over a 20-year period. The different shades of grey show how common the cancers were in each county compared with the rate for the country as a whole.

If you were concerned with researching the causes of stomach cancer and were using this map as a guide, where might you concentrate your research?

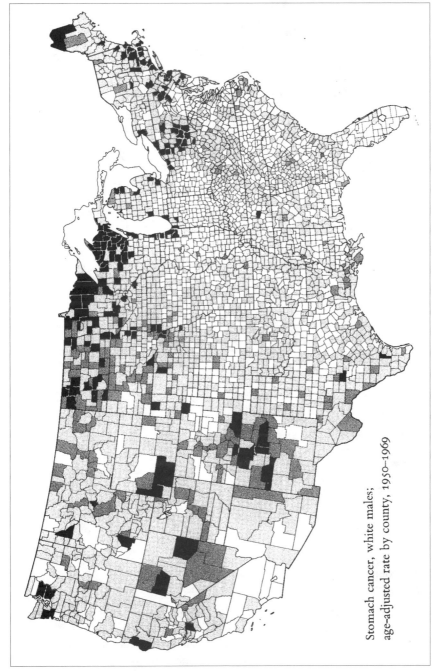

Stomach cancer, white males; age-adjusted rate by county, 1950–1969

Figure 34a

Commentary:

There are lots of possible answers here, and I've identified a few on the map below (*Figure 34b*). You could pick out high-incidence clusters: near the Great Lakes (top, just right of centre), scattered around the north-east corner, and toward the south-west (the large black areas slightly left and below centre).

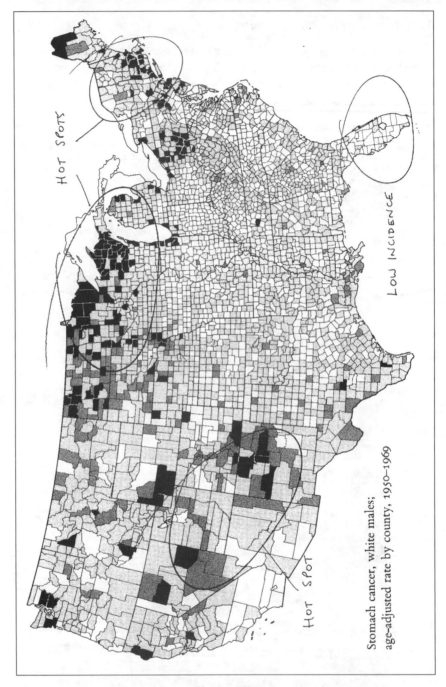

Figure 34b

On the other hand, there is a large area of relatively low incidence all across the lower right, and particularly in the Florida peninsula at bottom right.

There are two points here. First, this graphic contains an enormous amount of information, which would be difficult to present numerically. Second, and partly because of this, such presentations are a valuable source of hypotheses and insight: a way of seeing into the data. Combination with other graphics, for instance a similar map showing consumption of nitrites or smoked food, might make this map even more powerful as a source of hypotheses.

Using graphics to present data

Often someone thinks they know what the story is and they use a graphic to *tell* that story, rather than to *find* out about it. Here's an exercise in doing that.

ACTIVITY 46   ALLOW **10** MINUTES

Choosing an effective presentation

Here's some basic information: my mother is 77 years old, my wife is 45, I am 46, and we have three children aged 10 years, 3 years and 6 months. Select one of the graphics below to present information about the family's ages, and explain your choice.

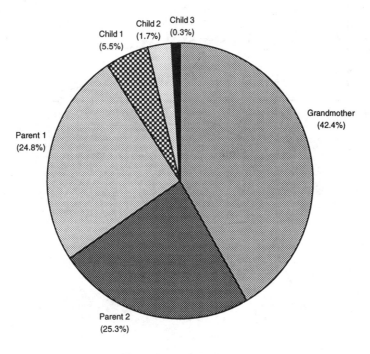

Figure 35a Family ages

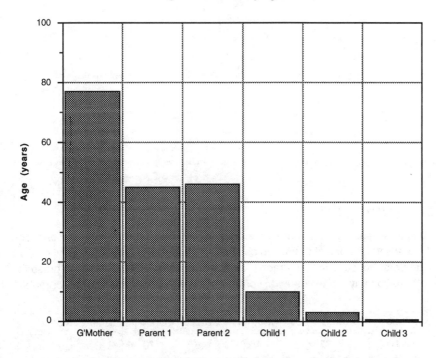

Figure 35b Family ages

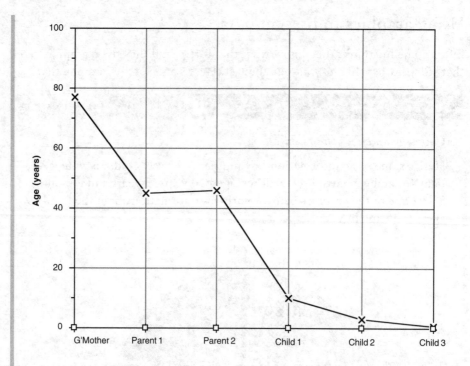

Figure 35c Family ages

Commentary:

This was a sneaky one. There are problems with each of these presentations. The best answer is none of them: you don't really need *any* graphic to present only six numbers. Constructing the graphic is not going to allow the audience to grasp the information any more clearly. My preference would be for a simple list or table:

Relation	Grandmother	Mother	Father	Child 1	Child 2	Child 3
Age (yrs)	77	45	46	10	3	0.5

Perhaps the original sentence was better still.

Only one of these graphics, the bar chart, makes any sense. The other two contain elements that don't make sense.

I'll start with the *line graph*: the problem here is that the various people have been set out along the bottom axis as though that was a real dimension, and that impression is strengthened by drawing lines between the various points. But that doesn't make sense: if we added a point to the line at the 60 year level, what would that mean? It would show something with an age of 60 – but what? It doesn't seem likely that it's a creature halfway between a mother and a grandmother. There are six separate individuals here and no justification for setting them out on a scale or suggesting that intermediate cases exist.

The *bar chart* doesn't suggest a dimension of 'persons' along its bottom axis. Each of the six individuals has their own bar, and there are no spurious connections between them. The problem here is in the vertical scale. In order to get both a 77-year-old and a six-month-old on the same scale, the vertical scale has to be compressed so much that the difference between 45 and 46 is only just apparent, and the youngest child hardly appears at all. The wide spread of the data makes it difficult to present it all in one graphic.

The *pie chart* also has this problem, but it also has a more fundamental one. Pie charts are useful for representing proportions of a whole. The 'whole' that has been used in constructing this pie chart is the total number of years all of the members of the family have been alive. The chart shows effectively that my mother has a large share of this whole, and the children much smaller shares. But since it's difficult to see what this 'whole' means, or why it's been chosen, the figure doesn't make sense. If I drew a similar pie chart of the number of articles of clothing owned by each member of the family, then the 'whole' – the total number of garments – does make sense, and the figure might be useful. If you were planning a new home for the family you could use it in allocating wardrobe space.

The primary point of this session is that graphics are only useful if they do more than the numerical presentation – for example, by allowing a lot of information to be presented in a small space, or by showing trends and patterns that aren't otherwise visible.

A secondary point is that not all graphs and charts are equally well suited to describing different types of data. You can find more detailed discussion in some of the references given at the end of the unit.

It's possible to force almost any set of data into almost any graphical presentation. Modern spreadsheets and computer packages make it possible to draw all kinds of complex graphics with just a few key presses. Before you do you should stop and ask:

- will this graphic do any good?

- does it add to what could be conveyed otherwise?

- does it make sense?

- are the data and the presentation logically consistent?

Distortion in graphical presentation

Whilst it's worth asking whether there is any point to using a graphic, another important question concerns the integrity of the graphic: does it show what it claims to show?

There are simple techniques for maximising or minimising the effect produced by a line graph. The next activity shows how this is done.

ACTIVITY 47 ALLOW **10** MINUTES

The importance of scale

Figure 36a is my redrawing of a graph that appeared in the press showing how road accidents have declined over the years. Use the data in *Table 9* to redraw the graph on the empty grid (*Figure 36b*).

Compare the two graphs and comment on the similarity, or otherwise, of the messages they convey.

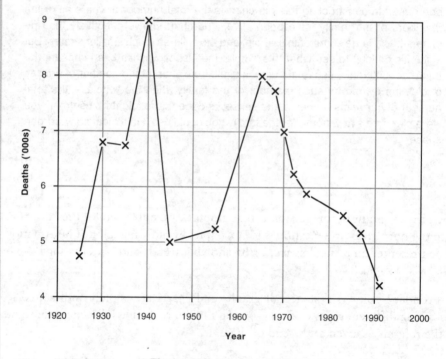

Figure 36a UK road deaths

Year	1925	'30	'35	'40	'45	'55	'65	'68	'70	'72	'76	'84	'88	'92
Deaths ('000s)	4.8	6.8	6.7	9.1	5	5.3	8	7.7	7	6.3	5.9	5.6	5.2	4.3

Table 9

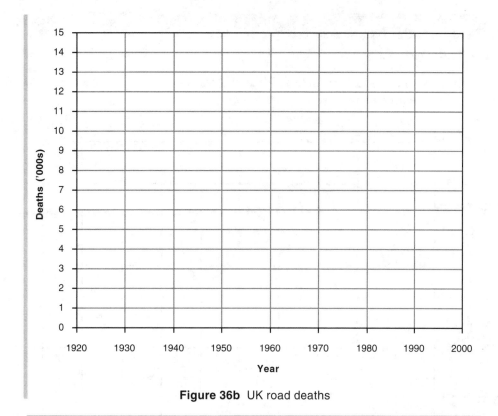

Figure 36b UK road deaths

Commentary:

The original graph gives the impression of a much larger fall in deaths, and a much lower present number of deaths than the redrawn version.

The information is the same, the general form of the graph is the same. The only thing that has changed is where the vertical scale starts. In the original it starts at 4,000; in the redrawn version it starts at zero (the starting point of the horizontal and vertical scales is called the origin).

The version with the origin at zero puts the changes in perspective with the overall figures: they're not that large, after all. The version with the origin of the vertical scale near the current level magnifies any changes as much as possible and ensures that the latest figure seems to be at a low level.

The choice of origin for either of the scales on a graph can have an enormous effect on the apparent meaning of the graph. The most straightforward version should have both scales starting at zero to show the figures in proportion to their actual values. If the horizontal scale shows time, then there should be some sensible reason for choosing the start point. Sometimes there's a natural zero, like birth, the start of treatment, or the first diagnosis of a disease. Sometimes some change in legislation, or a social or financial event, provides a natural start point.

I always advise people to be suspicious of graphs with scales which don't start at zero. Ask *why* the graph has been drawn like that: what would it look like if the origin was at zero? Often the answer to the first question is that nobody made a conscious decision about choosing the scales, but sometimes it's because the scales have been carefully chosen to produce just the effect that someone wanted to produce from the figures.

Sometimes there are good reasons for not having the origin at zero. I can think of two main ones. The next two activities are meant to bring out these two points.

ACTIVITY 48

Advantages of a non-zero origin

Examine the four figures below. What are the advantages, if any, of the versions with the non-zero origins?

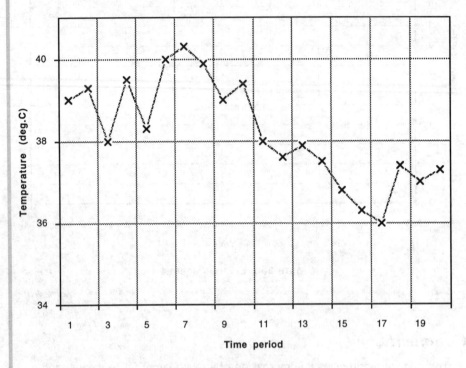

Figure 37a Patient temperature

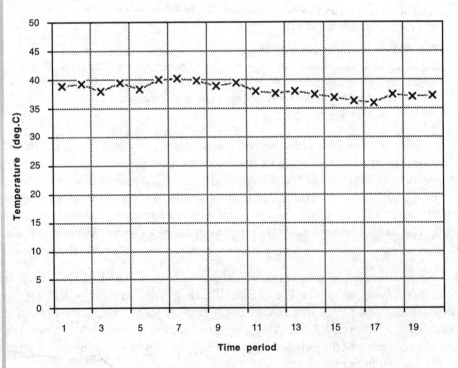

Figure 37b Patient temperature

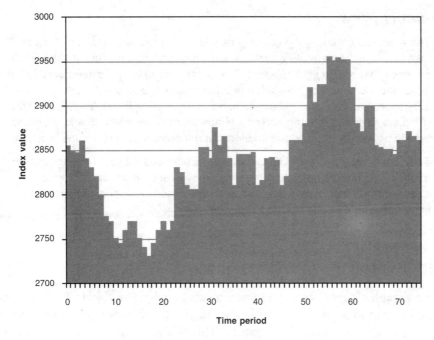

Figure 37c Financial index

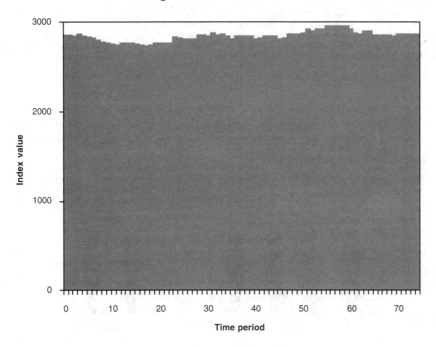

Figure 37d Financial index

Commentary:

The effect of not having the origin at zero is to magnify any small changes that take place. In the case of *Figure 37a* that's a good thing because it's the small changes that are really important. The difference between a temperature of 38°C and 42°C can be the difference between life and death. Even smaller differences can be diagnostically valuable. The zero-origin version (*Figure 37b*) gives the message that the person's temperature is 'between 35 and 40, going up and down a bit'. That's true enough, but not precise enough for the purpose.

The same applies to the financial figures. Enormous sums of money can be made by accurately predicting the small movements in the market which are exaggerated in the figure. If that's so, then the small movements are enormously important, and it's quite right to exaggerate them.

Representing people in graphics

When a graphic is representing information about people or objects, it often seems a good idea to make it more intelligible and visually interesting by using images of those things to convey the numbers. This is a good idea, but it has one big danger.

ACTIVITY 49   ALLOW **10** MINUTES

Height or volume?

The two graphics in *Figure 38* represent numbers of nurses on night duty per ward in two different years. The actual numbers are in brackets. Which represents the information most accurately? Why is there a difference in the accuracy of the representations?

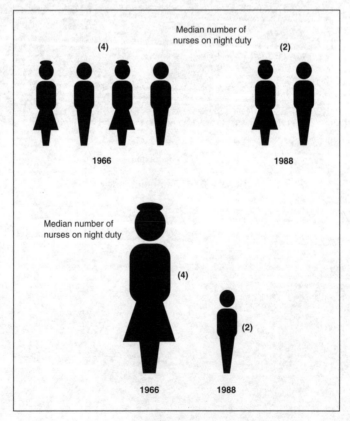

Figure 38

Commentary:

I prefer the upper version here: the number of people is represented by the number of people-like symbols in the graphic, and there is no chance of distortion.

In the lower version the numbers are represented by the heights of the symbols, and that in itself is reasonable. The problem arises because the symbol used is not a bar, which has an area on the page which changes in proportion with its height, but an image of a person. When the height increases, the width increases too. The left hand image in *b* has a height twice that of the right hand image. Its area is four times as great.

Worse than that, because it is an image of a person, it's difficult not to be influenced by the scale and solidity such sizes would have if they were real. A person twice as high as another will *weigh* many times more – perhaps six or eight times as much.

So the impression given by the lower figure is ambiguous. It shows a change of between a doubling and an eight-fold decrease, depending on which dimension of the figure you attend to. The strongest impression is of an enormous decrease in staffing levels – at least four-fold. The upper graphic gives the straightforward, clear version.

There are other problems with this use of realistic symbols to give information. If the mean staffing level had changed from 1.7 to 2.2, you would have to represent that by adding or removing small proportions from the people symbols, which would look odd.

When it's properly applied and carefully worked out, though, a system of using informative symbols like this can be a clear and accessible way of presenting information about numbers and quantities. In the 1940s, a full set of rules for doing this was worked out and called the *Isotype system*. It was used very effectively in geography books and atlases in the 1950s and 1960s.

There is much more to be said about ingenious, ingenuous and dreadful ways of presenting information graphically. If you would like to find out more, read some of the excellent books mentioned in the reading list.

Summary

1. Graphic presentations can be effective and powerful ways of conveying information, particularly from large or complicated data sets.

2. Graphics can be used to investigate data or to convey a message about data.

3. Graphic techniques can be used to distort the impression given by the figures.

4. This distortion can be helpful or confusing, depending on the nature of the figures and the purpose of the presentation.

5. The purpose of the presentation is the most important thing to bear in mind when choosing to use a graphic. Clarity and simplicity are also very important.

Before you move on to Session Nine, check that you have achieved the objectives given at the beginning of this session, and, if not, review the appropriate sections.

SESSION NINE

Reviewing your work

I'd like you to finish off this unit by summarising what you've learned through doing it.

Part of this process will be achieved by reviewing the knowledge and understanding of the specific points that have been raised in the sessions. You could do this in various ways:

- by writing your own definitions of the words in the glossary and comparing them with mine – better still, you could look up other people's definitions of the terms

- by making a list of the activity headings and going through it, trying to recall the point made by each one

- probably best, but most difficult – setting out to teach someone else all the material you've covered.

I have a final activity though that asks for a different kind of review – a review of general rather than specific points.

ACTIVITY 50

Descriptive statistics

Many general points have been made in this unit about the nature and use of descriptive statistics, and you should be able to make these points to other people.

Let's say that you have been asked to prepare a presentation on 'descriptive statistics and how they should be used' to a group who are mixed in their knowledge of and support for the use of descriptive statistics.

Using the objectives of the sessions as a starting point, map out the points you would make in your presentation, taking particular care over the source and use of the illustrations.

(You aren't expected to write an essay, just produce a plan on a single sheet of paper.)

Commentary:

This may be the most difficult activity in the unit. Here's my list of general points. It reflects my preferences and prejudices about statistics, so yours may differ considerably.

- The main purpose of descriptive statistics is for summarising information to make it easier to understand or represent.

- Information can be summarised to help to find out about what's going on, or to help to show others what's going on.

- There are a wide variety of techniques and approaches that can be used.

- Different approaches are useful for conveying or summarising different kinds of information.

- There is no absolute right way to present information statistically. Better ways are those that are best fitted for the purpose at hand.

- Because of this, it is a good idea to be clear about the purpose of using statistics before choosing the approach to use.

- Provided it fits with the last three points, the simplest and most straightforward presentation is best.

- Because they simplify or reorganise the original data, all statistical presentations distort the information to some extent. This is not necessarily a bad thing. Again, what is best depends on the purpose for which the statistics are being used. As with optical lenses, some distortion may help us see more clearly.

LEARNING REVIEW

	Not at all	Partly	Quite well	Very well

Session One

I can:

- explain that the reliability of data may be influenced by many factors ☐ ☐ ☐ ☐
- identify category, ranking and quantity measures ☐ ☐ ☐ ☐
- distinguish between interval and ratio scales. ☐ ☐ ☐ ☐

Session Two

I can:

- identify the various forms which statistical presentations may take ☐ ☐ ☐ ☐
- describe typical purposes for presenting information statistically. ☐ ☐ ☐ ☐

Session Three

I can:

- understand the importance of clearly defining what information I wish to obtain from data ☐ ☐ ☐ ☐
- group and rearrange data in a table in order to make sense of large amounts of information ☐ ☐ ☐ ☐
- identify ways of organising data and presenting it graphically using frequency distributions, pie charts and scattergrams. ☐ ☐ ☐ ☐

Session Four

I can:

- describe three main measures of central tendency: the mean, the mode and the median ☐ ☐ ☐ ☐
- explain the ways in which these measures are affected by changes in the data ☐ ☐ ☐ ☐
- select the most appropriate measure for particular purposes. ☐ ☐ ☐ ☐

Session Five

I can:

- use frequency distributions for summarising and presenting data ☐ ☐ ☐ ☐

- appreciate that the shape of a distribution is determined by the processes giving rise to it ☐ ☐ ☐ ☐

- describe typical deviations from ideal forms, such as skewedness, humps and dips, and be able to suggest reasons for them. ☐ ☐ ☐ ☐

Session Six

I can:

- understand that different sets of data have different degrees of internal variability ☐ ☐ ☐ ☐

- define the terms quartile, decile, and percentile ☐ ☐ ☐ ☐

- understand the way in which the standard deviation may be used to represent the variability in a set of figures ☐ ☐ ☐ ☐

- determine how common or rare a given value is compared to the overall sample from which it comes by using the standard deviation. ☐ ☐ ☐ ☐

Session Seven

I can:

- use scattergrams to detect trends and patterns in sets of data ☐ ☐ ☐ ☐

- describe the use of the correlation coefficient as a measure of the agreement between two sets of measures ☐ ☐ ☐ ☐

- state the meaning of positive and negative correlation ☐ ☐ ☐ ☐

- explain why the correlation coefficient does not always accurately represent the relationships between sets of observations ☐ ☐ ☐ ☐

- appreciate that correlation coefficients do not imply any causal relationship between factors. ☐ ☐ ☐ ☐

	Not at all	Partly	Quite well	Very well

Session Eight

I can:

- give three reasons for the graphical presentation of statistical data

	☐	☐	☐	☐

- select appropriate graphical presentations for various statistical purposes

	☐	☐	☐	☐

- describe two techniques which can be used to distort the impressions given in graphical presentations.

	☐	☐	☐	☐

FURTHER READING

General statistics

Most books in this area cover descriptive and inferential statistics. Some (even introductory ones) are heavily mathematical. Often the introductory ones have a few pages of non-mathematical introduction at the beginning of each chapter which are useful.

The ones I mention here are not very mathematical.

ROWNTREE D. 1981. *Statistics Without Tears*. Penguin, Harmondsworth.
  The subtitle is 'A Primer for Non-mathematicians' and I think that's right. This is excellent, clear and cheap. It goes slightly further into the maths than this unit, and covers inferential as well as descriptive statistics.

GWILLIAM P. 1988. *Basic Statistics*. Penguin, Harmondsworth.
  Slightly more formal in approach than Derek Rowntree's book. Still a good basic introduction which gives you lots of exercises to work through.

HOOKE R. 1983. *How To Tell The Liars From The Statisticians*. Dekker, New York.
  I enjoyed this book. It's a collection of short essays about various problems and paradoxes in statistics. It's not serious in tone, but it makes lots of serious points. The one disadvantage is that because of the way it's organised, it's difficult to find any specific topic, though there is an index.

PAULOS J. 1990. *Innumeracy*. Penguin, Harmondsworth.
  Not quite an introduction to statistics, though several statistical points are discussed. It's a short book on 'mathematical illiteracy and its consequences' which is useful background.

GOLDSTONE L. 1986. *Health and Nursing Management Statistics*. Newcastle on Tyne Polytechnic, Newcastle.
  Aimed at answering questions put by health service managers. Deals with many of the basic statistical issues as they arise in health care.

REID N., BOORE J. 1987. *Research Methods and Statistics in Health Care*. Arnold.
  A basic introduction with a 'how to do it' approach. The book has introductory sessions on descriptive and inferential statistics.

Presentation and graphics

HUFF D. 1973. *How To Lie With Statistics*. Penguin, Harmondsworth.
  Not just about graphics, but goes into all the ways in which statistics can mislead. Short and clear and well worth reading.

TUFTE E. 1983. *The Visual Presentation of Quantitative Information*. Graphics

Press, Cheshire, Connecticut.

The book is full of wonderful and ingenious examples of presenting information visually. Tufte discusses all the things that can go wrong in detail, and tries to develop some principles to ensure the best communication. Tufte's later book, *Envisioning Information*, from the same publisher, extends this approach to other kinds of material besides numerical information.

LOCKWOOD A. 1969. *Diagrams*. Studio Vista.

'A visual survey of graphs, maps, charts and diagrams for the graphic designer.' This is an old book, but it is a very thorough and sensible survey of the main ways of going about presenting information, with few words and lots of examples.

Sources of more material

Social Trends and *Regional Trends*, both published by the Central Statistical Office (and published by HMSO) every year, are full of fascinating information about the way we live now (and how we differ from each other). The information is presented in a variety of ways. You could go through and think of ways of improving the presentation – or just browse for statistical enjoyment.

GLOSSARY

Bimodal

A bimodal **distribution** has two local **modes**, that is, two values that are the most common values in their own section of the distribution. The two values need not be exactly the same, so only one of them will actually be the mode for the set of observations. As long as a distribution shows two distinct humps, it can be described as bimodal.

Correlation coefficient

A statistic used to express the similarity between two sets of observations. If measures of one variable tend to increase as measures of the other variable increase, the value of the correlation coefficient will be positive. (This is often shortened to 'the correlation is positive'.) If one set of values tends to decrease as the other increases, then the correlation will be negative. If there is no consistent pattern in the relationship between the two sets of measures, the correlation will be near zero. The value of the correlation coefficient can only vary over a range between +1 and -1.

Data

The set of observations or measurements that is being studied or statistically analysed.

Category variable

A measure which consists of putting observations into different groups, without any ranking or quantitative aspect. Recording numbers of complaints according to whether they occur in *medical, surgical, accident and emergency* or *community practice* is an example of using a category distinction.

Crosstabulated

A crosstabulated table is one in which the observations are grouped into more than one category on each of two variables. A table which divided numbers of workers up according to three different grades and also according to whether they had more or less than 10 years' work experience would be crosstabulated for grade and experience.

Decile

The measure that divides a ranked set of observations into groups that each contain 10%, or one tenth, of the observations. The first decile is the value that divides the bottom 10% of the observations from the rest. The 7th decile divides the bottom 70% from the top 30%. See also **quartile** and **percentile**.

Descriptive statistics

That part of statistics concerned with describing and representing data for the case at hand. This is in contrast with **inferential statistics**, which is concerned with establishing whether data provides a basis for making inferences or predictions about what is likely to happen in other cases.

Dispersion

The extent to which the values in a set of observations are different from each other. If all the values are similar, the dispersion is low. If there is a wide range of different values the dispersion is high. **Standard deviation** and **interquartile range** are **measures of dispersion**.

Distribution

A way of representing the pattern of observations in a set of data by setting them out in order in some way. The version used in this unit is the **frequency distribution**.

Frequency distribution

A **distribution** in which the number of observations at each value are counted up and then represented by the height of a line, bar or marker on a graph or chart.

Frequency table

A **distribution** in which the number of observations at each value are counted up and then represented by a number in a table. The non-graphical equivalent of **frequency distribution**.

Inferential statistics

That part of statistics concerned with establishing whether data provides a basis for making inferences or predictions about what is likely to happen in other cases. This is in contrast with **descriptive statistics**, which is concerned with describing and representing data for the case at hand.

Interquartile range

The difference between the first and third **quartiles**. A measure which defines the 50% of the observed values which are closest to the **median**. The interquartile range is a **measure of dispersion**.

Interval scale

A scale of measurement based on **quantity variables** in which the size of intervals between one measure and the next is constant, but there is no true zero, so the ratio between measures is not consistent.

Mean

A **measure of central tendency**. The mean is the value calculated by adding together all the observed values and then dividing by the number of observations. This is the value usually meant by 'average' in everyday language. The version described here is the *arithmetic* mean: there are other versions based on different ways of calculating the overall total. Other measures of central tendency are the **median** and the **mode**.

Measure of central tendency

A measure which helps to establish the middle, most common or average value of a set of observations. The three most commonly used measures of central tendency are the **mean**, the **median**, and the **mode**.

Measure of dispersion

A measure which helps to describe the amount of **dispersion**, or variability, in a set of observations. The **standard deviation** and the **interquartile range** are common measures of dispersion.

Median

A **measure of central tendency**. The median is the value that divides the rankings of all the observed cases in half, so that half the values are higher and half lower. It corresponds to the 50th **percentile**. Other measures of central tendency are the **mean** and the **mode**.

Midpoint of the range

The value in a set of observations which lies midway between the highest value and the lowest. Often confused with the **median**, which is the midpoint of the *rankings*, and quite different. The midpoint of the range is not a very useful statistic.

Modal

The adjective derived from **mode**. The modal value is that value which corresponds to the mode.

Mode

A **measure of central tendency**. The mode is the most common value among a set of observations. It is possible for there to be more than one mode for any set of figures. Other measures of central tendency are the **mean** and the **median**.

Multimodal

A multimodal **distribution** has several modes; that is, more than one value that is the most common value in the distribution. These values need not be exactly the same, so only one of them will actually be the mode for the set of observations. As long as a distribution shows several distinct humps, it can be described as multimodal.

Negative skew

A negatively skewed distribution has most values towards the higher end of the range of observations. In a **frequency distribution**, the shape is biased to the right.

Nominal scale

A scale of measurement which is based on categories alone, with no value or ranking attached to the measure.

Non-linear

A non-linear relationship is one in which the pattern of relationship between two variables does not follow a straight line. A common non-linear pattern is one in which values of one variable increase as the other increases, up to a certain point, but then one set of values levels off or falls with further increase of the other. The relationship between dosage and sense of well-being for some recreational drugs like alcohol follows a non-linear pattern.

Normal distribution

A particular mathematically defined frequency distribution. It is similar to those real-life distributions produced by summarising large numbers of random events. The normal distribution is symmetrical. The mean, median and mode are all at the same value. The relationship between the **standard deviation** and the proportion of observations in any part of the distribution is precisely defined. These well-defined features of the normal distribution are often useful in helping to analyse sets of real-life data which approximate to it (they are said to approximate to *normality*). *Normal* and *normality* in this sense have nothing to do with *normal* in the everyday sense.

Ordinal scale

A scale of measurement which is based on **ranking variables**. This should give information about which is greater or lesser, first or last, but without any information about the size of the difference between ranks.

Origin

The point at which the two axes, or baselines, of a graph cross. It is often at the zero point of the two scales, but does not necessarily have to be at that point.

Percentile

The measure that divides a ranked set of observations into groups that each contain 1%, or one hundredth, of the observations. The first percentile is the value that divides the bottom 1% of the observations from the rest. The 67th percentile divides the bottom 67% from the top 33%. See also **quartile** and **decile**.

Pie chart

A graphic representation of data in which the proportions of observations falling into different categories are shown as different sized sectors of a circle (or 'slices of a pie').

Positive skew

A positively skewed **distribution** has most values towards the lower end of the range of observations. In a **frequency distribution**, the shape is biased to the left.

Quantity variable

A measure which consists of assigning a numerical value to an observation, so that calculations and arithmetical comparisons with other values can justifiably be made. Recording the *number* of staff working in different units, the *temperature* of different environments, or the *time* between surgery and discharge are all examples of using quantity variables. Quantity variables can be subdivided into those based on **interval scales** and those based on **ratio scales**.

Quartile

The measure that divides a ranked set of observations into groups that each contain 25%, or a quarter, of the observations. The first quartile is the value that divides the bottom 25% of the observations from the rest. The 3rd quartile divides the bottom 75% from the top 25%. See also **decile, percentile** and **interquartile range**.

Range

The measure which is the difference between the largest observed value and the smallest. A fairly crude statistic, but sometimes useful. See also **interquartile range** and **midpoint of the range**.

Rank variable

A measure that assigns observations to an order from first to last, highest to lowest or most to least. Recording staff *rank* or *seniority*, or ratings of waiting rooms on a *scale of comfort*, are examples of using rank variables. An **ordinal scale** is based on rank variables.

Ratio scale

A scale of measurement based on **quantity variables** in which there is a constant relationship between steps of the scale and a true zero, so that it is possible to say that a measure which is twice as large represents a quantity which is twice as large.

Scattergram

A graphic in which the relationship between sets of measures of two variables is displayed by plotting each observation on a graph with one of the variables as the horizontal axis, and the other variable as the vertical axis. This produces a pattern of markers – one marker for each observation – from which any pattern in the relationship may be seen.

Significant

Unlikely to have arisen by chance. A significant result is one that can be used as a basis for making inferences about what will happen in future cases. Significance is a key concept in **inferential statistics**.

Skew

The extent to which a **distribution** is biased towards one end or other of the range of observations. The symmetrical **normal distribution** has no skew.

Standard deviation

A measure of **dispersion**. The greater the standard deviation, the greater the range of values observed. In the **normal distribution**, 68% of the observed values fall between one standard deviation above the mean and one standard deviation below the mean. The **interquartile range** is another measure of dispersion.

Unimodal

A unimodal distribution has a single **mode**. The **frequency distribution** will show one main hump.